# AUDIO AMPLIFIER CONSTRUCTION

CW00951898

# ALSO BY THE SAME AUTHOR

# AUDIO AMPLIFIER CONSTRUCTION

by
## R. A. PENFOLD

BERNARD BABANI (publishing) LTD
THE GRAMPIANS
SHEPHERDS BUSH ROAD
LONDON W6 7NF
ENGLAND

## PLEASE NOTE

Although every care has been taken with the production of this book to ensure that any projects, designs, modifications and/or programs etc. contained herein, operate in a correct and safe manner and also that any components specified are normally available in Great Britain, the Publishers do not accept responsibility in any way for the failure, including fault in design, of any project, design, modification or program to work correctly or to cause damage to any other equipment that it may be connected to or used in conjunction with, or in respect of any other damage or injury that may be so caused, nor do the Publishers accept responsibility in any way for the failure to obtain specified components.

Notice is also given that if equipment that is still under warranty is modified in any way or used or connected with home-built equipment then that warranty may be void.

Due to printing processes used during the manufacture of this book, the Publishers cannot guarantee the absolute accuracy with which the PCB track patterns are reproduced.

© 1983 BERNARD BABANI (publishing) LTD

First Published — December 1983

**British Library Cataloguing in Publication Data**
Penfold, R. A.
    Audio amplifier construction. — (BP122)
    1. Amplifiers, Audio
    I. Title
    621.389'3      TK9968

    ISBN 0 85934 097 X

Printed and bound in Great Britain by Cox & Wyman Ltd, Reading

# Preface

Despite the progressive broadening of electronics as a hobby with new spheres of interest constantly emerging, audio amplifiers of various types seem to be more popular than ever. One reason for this is probably the continuing popularity of hi-fi and budget audio equipment. Another is simply that audio amplifiers form an important part of many items of equipment other than hi-fi and low cost audio equipment.

The purpose of this book is to provide a range of preamplifier and power amplifier designs which will, between them, cover most applications and requirements. The preamplifier circuits include low noise microphone and RIAA types, a tape head preamplifier, as well as tone controls. Power amplifiers from low power battery operated circuits to high power MOSFET types are included, as well as a 12 volt bridge amplifier capable of giving up to 18 watts RMS.

All the circuits are easy to construct using the printed circuit or 0.1 in. matrix stripboard designs provided. Where necessary any setting up procedures are described, but in most cases no setting up or test gear is required in order to successfully complete the project. The MOSFET power amplifiers are an exception, but even these only require an ordinary multimeter for initially testing for the correct bias current. Thus most of the projects are within the capabilities of constructors of limited experience, and they are not just for more advanced readers who require a collection of audio circuits.

*R. A. Penfold*

# CONTENTS

# Chapter 1

# PREAMPLIFIERS

In this chapter a number of preamplifier circuits will be described including tone control circuits, and there should be a suitable design here for virtually any normal audio preamplifier application.

## Microphone Preamp.

Where high quality is required the most common types of microphone in use these days are probably electret types having a built-in preamplifier and step-up transformer, or dynamic types having a built-in step-up transformer. In either case the output level of the microphone is not normally very high, with a signal amplitude of only around 2 millivolts RMS being typical. This is far too small to permit such microphones to be used successfully with many items of audio equipment where the most sensitive input might require an input level of a few hundred millivolts RMS. Incidentally, although some items of equipment have an input for a magnetic pick-up with an input sensitivity of around 2 to 5 millivolts RMS, as we shall see later, an input of this type has a tailored frequency response and will not give satisfactory results if fed from a microphone.

This microphone preamplifier has a voltage gain of over 52dB (400 times) and will match a high impedance dynamic or electret microphone to virtually any piece of audio equipment. When used in conjunction with most microphones of these types an output level of about 1 volt RMS can be readily achieved, but a gain control enables a lower output level to be set so that overloading of the equipment fed with the output signal can be avoided. The signal to noise ratio of the unit is excellent, and is typically well over 70dB with reference to an output level of 1 volts RMS (at full gain, unweighted). As will be explained later, the circuit can be modified for use with a low impedance dynamic microphone or an electret type which does not have an integral step-up transformer.

The full circuit diagram of the Microphone Preamplifier is shown in Figure 1.

The circuit is a two stage type which uses IC1 as a non-inverting amplifier, and IC2 as an inverting amplifier (both are operational amplifiers of course). Both amplifiers are standard configurations. The closed loop gain of IC1 is set at about 45 times by negative feedback circuit R3 and R5. The input impedance of the circuit is set at a nominal figure of 27k by R4, and this is high enough to ensure that excessive loading of the microphone does not occur. C2 provides DC blocking at the input of the circuit. A set of break contacts on input jack JK1 are used to short circuit the input when no microphone is connected to the unit. This eliminates any stray pick-up of electrical noise at the input, and also prevents possible oscillation due to stray feedback. The device used in the IC1 position is a NE5534 or NE5534A high performance operational amplifier. The NE5534A is slightly better than the NE5534 for audio applications such as this one (although it is a little more expensive), but both devices give excellent performance with very low levels of noise and distortion. The circuit will work using other low noise, internally compensated operational amplifiers such as the 741C or TL071CP, but the noise performance of the NE5534 or NE5534A is noticeably superior to most of the alternative devices, and the additional cost of an NE5534 or NE5534A is usually well justified in a critical application such as this.

C3 couples the output of IC1 to VR1 which is a simple volume control type gain control. From here C4 couples the signal to the second stage of amplification. R6 and R9 form a negative feedback circuit which set the closed loop voltage gain of IC2 at ten times, giving the circuit a maximum total voltage gain of about 450 times. As far as noise performance is concerned, the ultimate in performance is not required from the device employed in the IC2 position since the signal level at the input to this stage is far higher than that at the input of IC1. Using a really low noise device here would not give any noticeable improvement in noise performance, and the TL081CP (or a similar device such as the LF351) give a more than adequate level of performance. BIFET operational amplifiers such as the TL081CP and LF351 have very low levels of distortion, and the distortion produced

2

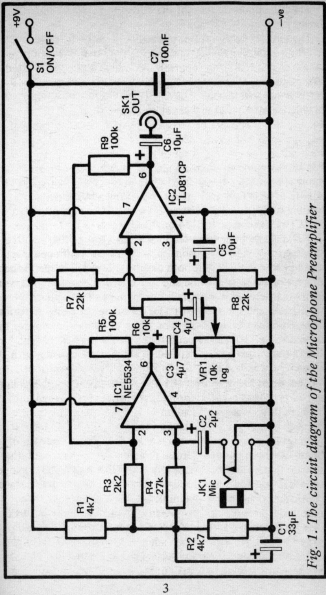

Fig. 1. The circuit diagram of the Microphone Preamplifier

3

by the circuit is negligible provided the output level does not exceed about 2 volts RMS or so.

The current consumption of the circuit is about 6 milliamps, and this can be supplied economically by even a small 9 volt battery such as a PP3 or PP6 type. A higher supply potential of up to 30 volts can be used and a higher supply voltage gives the circuit a larger overload margin, but the current consumption increases somewhat at higher supply voltages.

## Construction

A printed circuit board measuring 3.2 inches by 1.7 inches takes all the components except VR1 and the sockets. Figure 2 gives details of the component layout and wiring while Figure 3 shows the copper track pattern. The board is constructed in the normal way and is perfectly straight forward.

It may be possible to build the unit into some other item of equipment, or you may wish to construct it as a self contained preamplifier. If the latter is the case it is advisable to house the unit in a metal case which gives good screening from sources of electrical interference such as mains hum. A diecast aluminium box is ideal, and these also have the advantage of being extremely tough. SK1 can be any convenient type of two way audio connector (jack, phono, etc.), but as JK1 must be fitted with a break contact this really restricts the choice here to a standard 6.35mm or a 3.5mm jack, and the microphone plug must be changed accordingly if necessary.

## Low Impedance Version

As mentioned earlier, the circuit can be modified to suit a low impedance microphone such as a dynamic type which does not have an internal step-up transformer, and this simply entails a few changes in component values. The input impedance of the circuit does not need to be as high for a low impedance microphone, and R4 can therefore be reduced in value to 2k2. In order to maintain a good low frequency response C2 should be increased to $10\mu F$ in value. The gain of the circuit needs to be increased since the circuit must compensate for the loss of voltage gain provided by the step-up transformer in a high

4

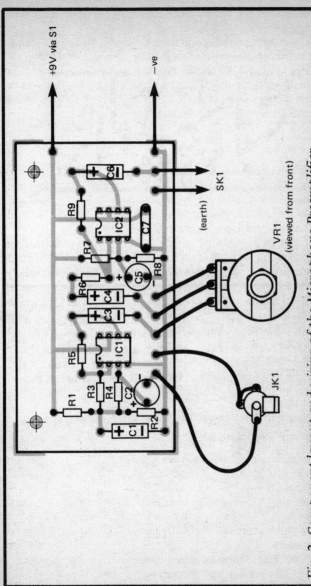

Fig. 2. Component layout and wiring of the Microphone Preamplifier

+9V via S1

−ve

SK1

(earth)

VR1
(viewed from front)

JK1

5

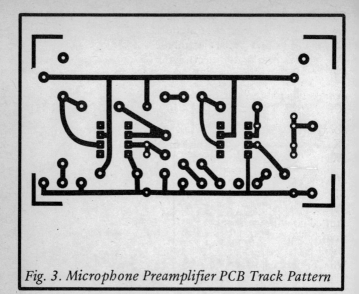

*Fig. 3. Microphone Preamplifier PCB Track Pattern*

impedance microphone. This can be accomplished by raising the value of R9, say to about 470k. An inevitable consequence of this boost in gain is a significant reduction in signal to noise ratio, although the circuit should be quite acceptable in this respect. However, wherever possible it is better to use a high impedance microphone and the circuit values shown in Figure 1.

*Components for Microphone Preamplifier (Figure 1)*

*Resistors,* all miniature ¼ watt 5%

| R1 | 4k7 | R2 | 4k7 |
|----|------|----|------|
| R3 | 2k2 | R4 | 27k |
| R5 | 100k | R6 | 10k |
| R7 | 22k | R8 | 22k |
| R9 | 100k | | |
| VR1 | 10k log. carbon potentiometer | | |

*Capacitors*

| C1 | 33µF 16V axial electrolytic |
|----|------|
| C2 | 2µ2 50V radial electrolytic |

C3      4μ7 50V axial electrolytic
C4      4μ7 50V axial electrolytic
C5      10μF 16V radial electrolytic
C6      10μF 16V axial electrolytic
C7      100nF polyester

*Semiconductors*
IC1      NE5534 or NE5534A      IC2      TL081CP or LF351

*Sockets*
JK1      3.5mm jack with single break contact
SK1      2 way audio connector

*Miscellaneous*
S1      SPST miniature toggle switch
Case
Printed circuit board
Control knob
9 volt battery (e.g. PP3)
Wire, battery connector, etc.

**Tape Preamplifier**

When used in conjunction with a suitable power supply and a
cassette mechanism this simple playback amplifier makes a
useful cassette player for use with a hi-fi system.  Suitable
cassette mechanisms are available quite cheaply on the surplus
market from time to time, or it may be possible to obtain a
suitable mechanism from a defunct cassette recorder.  Alternatively
a new cassette mechanism could be used, and these are available
from one or two companies.

*Equalisation*

Due to the low output signal level of a tape head and the
comparatively high drive voltage required by most hi-fi
amplifiers, a tape playback amplifier must give both high gain
and a low noise level.  Furthermore, the output from a tape
head requires equalisation since it provides an output that
increases at a rate of 6dB per octave (i.e. a doubling of frequency

causes the output voltage to be doubled). This is because a doubling in frequency causes a doubling in the rate at which the magnetic field changes, and the output voltage is dependent on both the field intensity and rate of change. This is actually the same effect that is obtained with a magnetic cartridge in a record player.

However, whereas a magnetic pick-up and a record work efficiently over the entire audio band, this is not true of normal magnetic tape systems. These become very inefficient at higher audio frequencies so that the rise in output first slows up, and then actually turns over to give a reduction in output. To a certain extent this reduction in efficiency is overcome by applying treble boost to the recorded signal, but this is not sufficient to maintain a 6dB per octave rise over the whole audio band.

In cassette systems the output from the tape head rises normally up to a frequency of approximately 2kHz, and then hardly increases at all at higher frequencies. The tape playback amplifier must therefore have a frequency response which is the inverse of this, and the required response is shown in Figure 4. The slight roll-off at the low end of the response only really effects sub-audio signals, and is used merely to prevent any signals of this type from giving rise to undesirable effects. It also makes it easier to avoid low frequency instability.

## The Circuit

Figure 5 shows the circuit diagram of the Tape Preamplifier, and this is for one channel only. The other channel is, of course, essentially the same.

An LM382 dual audio preamplifier integrated circuit is used at the input of the unit, one section of the device being used in each stereo channel. The pin numbers shown in Figure 5 are for the left hand channel; those for the right hand channel being shown in brackets. The supply connections are common to both channels. The LM382 is well suited to this application as it provides a low noise level, low distortion, and high gain. It is also quite inexpensive, and is a convenient point at which to add the equalisation.

The equalisation is provided by R2 and C6 which are

8

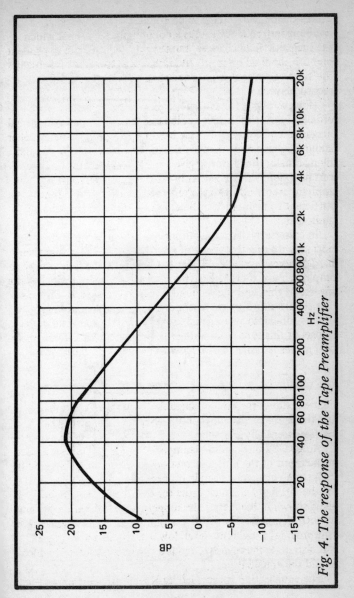

Fig. 4. The response of the Tape Preamplifier

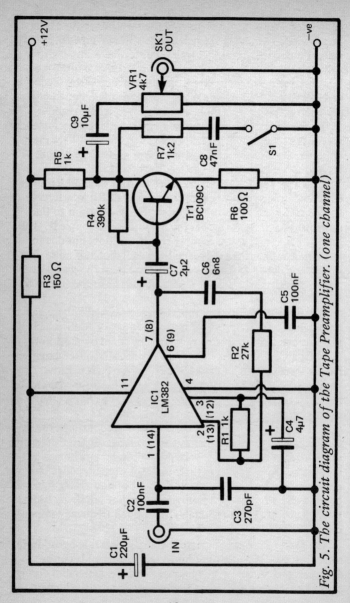

Fig. 5. The circuit diagram of the Tape Preamplifier. (one channel)

10

connected between the output and the inverting input of the preamplifier. At low frequencies C6 has a high impedance which consequently gives a low level of feedback and high voltage gain. At higher frequencies the impedance of C6 becomes progressively lower, giving increased negative feedback and rolling off the response of the circuit at the required 6dB per octave. This only continues up to a frequency of about 2kHz, as above this frequency the impedance of C6 becomes very low in comparison to that of R2, and does not have much effect on the level of feedback or voltage gain of the circuit. R1 and C4 are also part of the feedback circuit.

C2 is the input DC blocking capacitor and C3 is an RF filter capacitor which helps to avoid problems with RF interference and instability due to stray feedback from the output to the non-inverting input (to which the input signal is coupled). The LM382 has a high level of supply ripple rejection, but due to the very low input signal level and the likelyhood of noise spikes being coupled into the supply lines from the motor in the cassette mechanism, C1 and R3 are used to filter the supply to IC1.

Although IC1 provides a substantial amount of voltage gain it still gives an output level of only about 50mV RMS, which is about one tenth of the drive voltage required by most hi-fi amplifiers. Tr1 is therefore used as a common emitter amplifier having a voltage gain of about 20dB. R4 provides negative feedback which reduces the voltage gain of Tr1 to the correct level and also gives a lower distortion level. C9 couples the output of Tr1 to variable output attenuator VR1.

It is likely that many of the cassettes played through the unit will be Dolby B encoded types, but unfortunately there are difficulties in incorporating a Dolby B decoder in a home-constructed cassette player (licensing, adjustment, added cost and complexity). However, a certain amount of noise reduction can be obtained when playing Dolbyised cassettes simply by using a treble cut filter, and a reasonably flat overall frequency response can be obtained.

The Dolby B process operates by applying treble boost during recording, but the amount of boost applied depends on the dynamic level of the recorded signal. It is at a maximum during periods of low signal level, and reduces to zero at the highest

11

dynamic levels. On playback the decoder applies treble cut to the signal, and the degree of treble cut again varies with dynamic level. In fact the treble cut exactly compensates for the treble boost used when recording so that a flat frequency response is produced. However, the treble cut used during playback reduces tape "hiss" during quiet passages when it is most intrusive. There is no noise reduction when the signal is at the highest dynamic levels, but this is unimportant since the noise is then totally masked by the signal anyway.

In this circuit S1 is closed when a Dolby B encoded cassette is played, and this switches into circuit a simple top cut filter which is comprised of R7 and C8. This filter gives an attenuation of about 5dB at frequencies of about 10kHz or more. The attenuation steadily decreases at lower frequencies, and is insignificant at middle and low frequencies. This results in high frequencies being boosted by about 5dB during periods of low signal level, and attenuated by about 5dB during periods of maximum dynamic level. At medium signal levels there is a roughly flat frequency response. Thus this simple arrangement gives a small but worthwhile reduction in noise plus a reasonably flat overall frequency response.

The performance of the playback amplifier is very good, but it must be borne in mind that the level of performance obtained from the player is determined by other factors such as the performance of the cassette mechanism, the playback head used, the recording tape, etc. The prototype gave very acceptable results when tried with good quality recordings and a surplus from loading cassette mechanism.

## Power Supply

The mains power supply circuit shown in Figure 6 is ideal for use with the Tape Preamplifier, and provided a 12 volt cassette mechanism is used it will power this as well. It can provide a maximum current of about 400 milliamps which is sufficient to operate any normal cassette mechanism even during fast-forward or fast-rewind (when the current consumption is at its highest).

The circuit is quite straight forward and uses full wave (bridge) rectification and a 12 volt monolithic voltage regulator

12

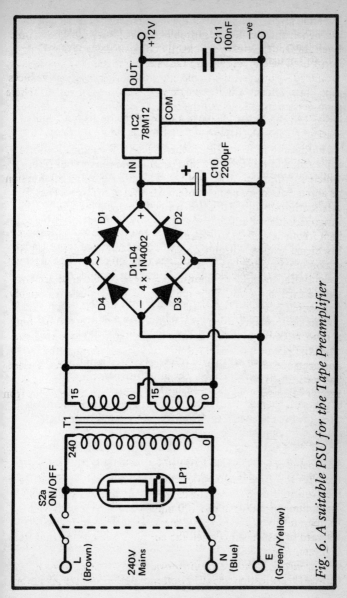

*Fig. 6. A suitable PSU for the Tape Preamplifier*

13

to give a well smoothed and stabilised output. T1 is one of the common twin secondary types, and in this circuit the two secondaries are connected in parallel to effectively give a 15 volt 400 milliamp winding.

## Construction

Both channels of the playback amplifier can be accommodated on a 0.1in. matrix stripboard panel which has 41 holes by 18 copper strips. Figure 7 shows the component layout of this panel while Figure 8 shows the points at which the copper strips must be cut. Many of the component identifications are repeated in Figure 7, and this is where two of each component are required, one for each stereo channel. The only connections not shown in Figure 7 are the wires from the sliders of VR1 to the output sockets (which were phono types on the prototype, but can be any preferred type). Of course, the two input leads must be screened, and in the interest of good channel separation it is advisable to use either separate leads or twin individually screened lead.

A suitable 0.1in. pitch stripboard layout for the power supply is shown in Figure 9, and this is based on a board which has 11 copper strips by 15 holes. There are no breaks in any of the copper strips.

Due to the high sensitivity of the playback amplifier, especially at low frequencies, the amplifier panel is quite sensitive to stray pick up of mains hum and other electrical noise. It is therefore advisable to mount the board where it is a reasonable distance away from T1 and the motor in the cassette mechanism.

IC2 requires a small amount of heatsinking and it may be possible to use the case as a heatsink if a metal type is used. Alternatively a small finned (bolt on) heatsink should be adequate, and a heatsink of this type was used on the prototype.

In use VR1 will probably need to be adjusted for maximum output in order to give good results. However, a few amplifiers have high sensitivity and with such units it will be necessary to back-off VR1 somewhat, otherwise the volume control of the amplifier will operate rather abruptly.

It is just possible that the output of the unit will not be high

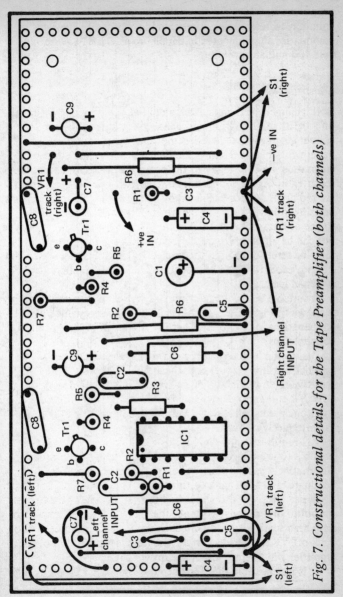

Fig. 7. Constructional details for the Tape Preamplifier (both channels)

15

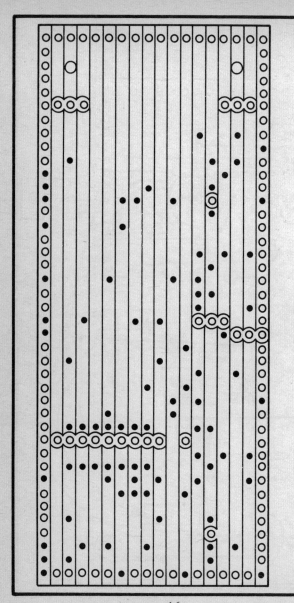

Fig. 8. The underside of the component board

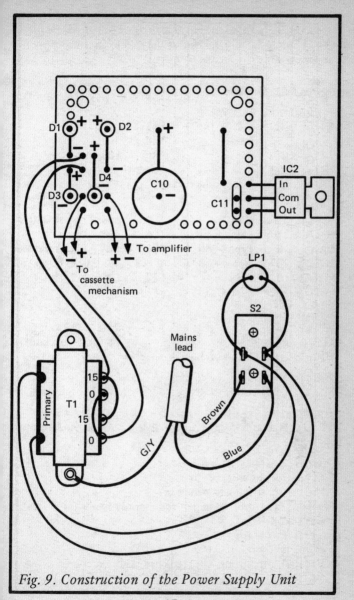

Fig. 9. Construction of the Power Supply Unit

17

enough to drive some amplifiers properly. If this should be the case a simple solution to the problem is to reduce the two R6s to 47 ohms in value. This boosts the gain of the output amplifiers and gives increased output.

*Components for Tape Preamp and Power Supply (Figure 5 & 6)*

*Resistors,* all ¼ watt 5%

| *R1 | 1k | *R2 | 27k |
|------|------|------|------|
| R3 | 150 ohms | *R4 | 390k |
| *R5 | 1k | *R6 | 100 ohms |
| *R7 | 1k2 | | |
| VR1 | 4k7 log. dual gang carbon | | |

*Capacitors*

| C1 | 220µF 25V | *C2 | 100nF type C280 |
|------|------|------|------|
| *C3 | 270pF ceramic plate | *C4 | 4µ7 25V |
| *C5 | 100nF type C280 | *C6 | 6n8 polystyrene 5% |
| *C7 | 2µ2 25V | *C8 | 47nF type C280 |
| *C9 | 10µF 25V | C10 | 2200µF 25V |
| C11 | 100nF type C280 | | |

*Semiconductors*

| IC1 | LM382 | IC2 | 78M12 (12 volt 500mA |
|------|------|------|------|
| *Tr1 | BC109C | | positive regulator) |
| D1 to D4 | 1N4002 (4 off) | | |

*Switches*

| S1 | DPST rotary switch | S2 | DPST toggle switch |
|------|------|------|------|

*Transformer*

T1       Standard mains primary, twin 15 volt 200mA secondari

*Miscellaneous*

Case

Two control knobs

0.1in. matrix stripboard panels

Panel indicator neon having integral series resistor for normal mains useage (LP1)

Cassette mechanism (see text)

Two phono output sockets

Mains lead, connecting wire, screened lead, solder, etc.

(Note that where a component is marked "*", two of this item are required, one for each stereo channel).

## Guitar Preamplifier

The output signal level from guitar pick-ups seems to vary quite considerably from one pick-up to another, and while some provide a very high output which can drive practically any power amplifier, others provide an output of only about 30 millivolts RMS or so. Amplifiers specifically designed for use with guitars normally have a fairly high sensitivity so that they can be used successfully with practically any pick-up, but when using a guitar with some other type of amplifier (such as a hi-fi amplifier) it is often found that the maximum volume obtained is inadequate.

A simple solution to the problem is to use a preamplifier to boost the signal level prior to feeding it to the power amplifier. The simple design described here has a voltage gain which can be varied from unity to over 26dB (20 times), and it should therefore match virtually any guitar pick-up to virtually any power amplifier. The input impedance of the preamplifier is about 50k and the output impedance is low. Thus the circuit can be used with unity voltage gain as a simple buffer amplifier, if it is necessary, to match the relatively high output impedance of a guitar pick-up to a power amplifier having a low input impedance.

### The Circuit

A single low noise BIFET operational amplifier (IC1) is used as the basis of the unit which consequently has negligible distortion levels and a signal to noise ratio that will be about -70dB or more even if the unit is used with a very low output guitar. Figure 10 shows the full circuit diagram of the Guitar Preamplifier.

This is just a straight forward operational amplifier non-inverting mode circuit with R2 and R3 being used to bias the non-inverting input of IC1 to about half the supply voltage. These also set the input impedance of the circuit at about 50k. R1 and R4 are the negative feedback network, and with R4 at

19

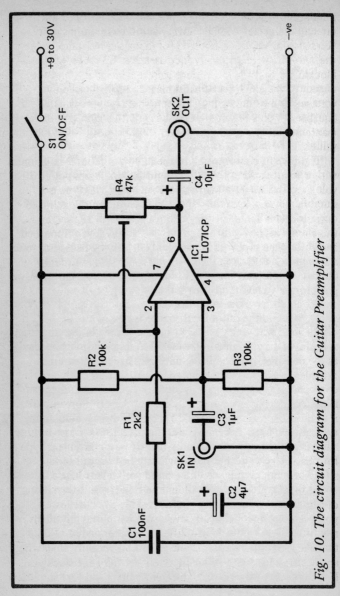

Fig. 10. The circuit diagram for the Guitar Preamplifier

20

minimum value the inverting input and output of IC1 are directly connected to one another and the circuit has unity voltage gain. As R4 is adjusted for increased resistance value the AC voltage gain steadily increases, but C2 provides DC blocking so that the DC voltage gain remains unity, and the output of the amplifier remains biased at half the supply voltage. The voltage gain of the amplifier is approximately equal to R1 plus R4, divided by R1, and this gives a nominal maximum voltage gain of just over 22 times with R4 at maximum value.

The current consumption of the circuit is about 2 milliamps with a 9 volt supply, rising to around 2.5 milliamps with a 30 volt supply. A small 9 volt battery such as a PP3 type is a suitable power source for the unit. The maximum unclipped output level is about 2 volts RMS using a 9 volt supply, and this should be perfectly adequate. Note that a well smoothed and ripple free supply is required, and it may be necessary to use a simple R – C filter in the positive supply lead in order to obtain a low level of mains hum on the output if a simple mains power supply is used.

## Construction

A 0.1in. matrix stripboard having 22 holes by 13 strips is used as the constructional basis of the amplifier, and Figure 11 provides full details of this board. Construction of the component panel is carried out using the usual techniques and is perfectly straight forward. As for any sensitive preamplifier, it is advisable to use a metal case such as a diecast aluminium type. SK1 and SK2 were both 6.35mm jacks on the prototype, and although these will probably be the most convenient type for this application, they can obviously be changed for an alternative type if this would be more convenient in use.

For optimum results R4 should be set for the lowest level of gain that gives satisfactory results. This gives the lowest possible noise and distortion levels, and minimises any slight risk of problems with the amplifier being overloaded. Note that the gain of the circuit is unity with R4 set fully clockwise, and at maximum with this component set fully anticlockwise. If the unit is to be used with different guitars and (or) amplifiers

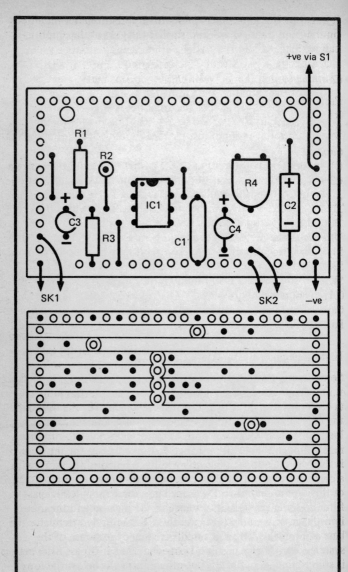

Fig. 11. Constructional details of the Guitar Preamp

22

it might be better to replace R4 with a potentiometer mounted on the front panel of the unit so that the gain of the amplifier can be adjusted more easily.

*Components for Guitar Preamplifier (Figure 10)*

*Resistors*, ¼ watt 5% except R4

| | | | |
|---|---|---|---|
| R1 | 2k2 | R2 | 100k |
| R3 | 100k | R4 | 47k 0.1 watt horizon preset |

*Capacitors*

| | | | |
|---|---|---|---|
| C1 | 100nF polyester | C2 | 4µ7 50V axial electrolytic |
| C3 | 1µF 50V rad. electrolytic | C4 | 10µF 25V rad. electrolytic |

*Semiconductor*
IC1   TL071CP

*Miscellaneous*
S1    SPST toggle switch
SK1   6.35mm jack
SK2   6.35mm jack
0.1in. matrix stripboard
Case
Battery, battery connector, wire, etc.

## High Impedance Buffer Amplifier

Sometimes an amplifier having an extremely high input impedance is required, such as when using a crystal or ceramic pick-up, or at the input of a piece of audio test equipment. In the case of the latter the high input impedance is needed since minimal loading of the circuit under test is essential in order to produce reliable results. With ceramic and crystal pick-ups the problem is that the pick-up is effectively a voltage generator in series with a capacitor of typically 2 to 20 nanofarads in value. If a pick-up of this type is fed into a low impedance load a simple highpass filter is formed by the capacitance of the pick-up and the input impedance of the amplifier, and this filter severely attenuates the bass and possibly even the middle frequency response of the system. With a very high load impedance the highpass filter action is still produced, but as the cut-off frequency is below the lower limit of the audio spectrum this is of no practical significance.

The buffer amplifier featured here has a very high input impedance of typically over 100 megohms at 1kHz, and the input impedance can be easily changed to any desired figure below this level. The voltage gain of the circuit is unity.

## The Circuit

Figure 12 shows the circuit diagram of the High Impedance Buffer Amplifier, and the unit is basically just an operational amplifier used as a unity gain non-inverting amplifier. By coupling the output of IC1 direct to its inverting input 100% negative feedback is applied over the device so that the required unity voltage gain and very high input impedance are obtained. However, the bias circuit, which in this case consists of R1 to R3, shunts the input impedance of the amplifier so that the circuit as a whole has a far lower input impedance than IC1 alone. The input impedance is still around 2.7 megohms, and this is adequate for most applications.

The shunting effect of the bias resistors can be eliminated though, and this is the purpose of "bootstrapping" capacitor C2. This couples the output signal to the junction of the three bias resistors, and any change in input voltage is therefore matched by an identical change in voltage at the output of IC1 and at the junction of the three bias resistors. This gives a constant voltage across R3, and any change in the voltage at one end of R3 produced by the input signal is counteracted by an identical change in potential at the other end of R3. This resistor has an apparent infinite resistance as far as the input signal is concerned since this signal does not generate any potential difference across R3 or produce any current flow through this component, and the shunting effect of the bias resistors is totally eliminated.

A standard 741C operational amplifier is used in the IC1 position, and as mentioned earlier this gives an input impedance which is typically in excess of 100 megohms at 1kHz, which should be more than adequate for any normal application. The higher input impedance that could be obtained using a FET input operational amplifier is not really of any practical value, and there are a couple of disadvantages to using most FET input devices in this circuit. One is simply that they have a tendency

24

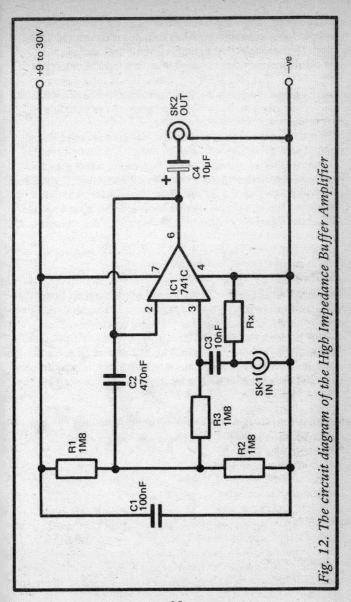

Fig. 12. The circuit diagram of the High Impedance Buffer Amplifier

to oscillate when the input is open circuit (the oscillations are damped down and removed when an input is connected to the unit). The second is that most FET input devices have a significantly higher input capacitance than bipolar devices such as the 741C. Thus the shunting effect of this capacitance would actually give a lower input impedance at most frequencies, and would only give a higher input impedance at lower-middle and bass frequencies.

If a comparitively low input impedance is required for some reason (such as for use with pick-up which has a recommended load impedance of several hundred kilohms or a few megohms) one way of achieving this is to remove C2 and adjust the values of R1 to R3 to give the desired input impedance. A simple alternative is to simply add resistor Rx, and the input impedance will be approximately equal to the value of the component used here.

## Construction

The buffer amplifier is built on a small printed circuit board, as detailed in Figures 13 and 14, and construction should present no difficulties. There is provision on the board for resistor Rx incidentally. The circuit will operate satisfactorily from any supply potential from 9 to 30 volts with a current consumption of about 2 milliamps. The maximum peak to peak output voltage is about 4 volts less than the supply voltage.

*Components for High Impedance Buffer Stage (Figure 12)*
*Resistors,* all ¼W 10%

| R1 | 1M8 | R2 | 1M8 |
|----|-----|----|-----|
| R3 | 1M8 | | |
| Rx | See text | | |

*Capacitors*

| C1 | 100nF polyester | C2 | 470nF carbonate |
|----|-----------------|----|-----------------|
| C3 | 10nF polyester | C4 | 10$\mu$F 25V axial electrolytic |

*Semiconductor*

| IC1 | 741C |
|-----|------|

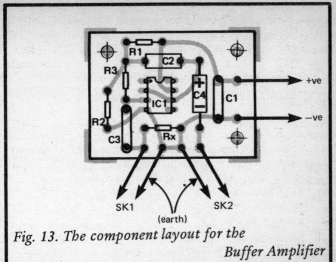

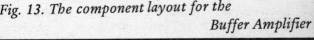

*Fig. 13. The component layout for the*
*Buffer Amplifier*

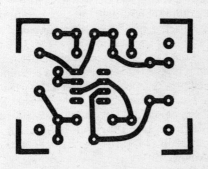

*Fig. 14. Buffer Amplifier PCB track pattern*

*Miscellaneous*
Case
Printed circuit board
Input and output sockets (SK1 and SK2)
Wire, etc.

## Tone Controls

A tone control or tone controls seems to be a feature of almost every audio amplifier regardless of its intended application, and even quite simple pieces of audio equipment such as portable cassette players and radios seem to have a simple tone control these days. Tone controls range from a simple top-cut control which can be used to attenuate high frequencies and reduce background "hiss" to graphic equalisers. Probably the most common and popular type of tone control system is the type where there are separate bass and treble controls which are each capable of providing several dB of boost or cut. These give a great deal of control over the reproduced sound, but need only quite simple and inexpensive circuitry.

The tone controls described here are of this normal bass and treble type, and the next section of this book covers a simple central tone control which can be used in conjunction with this design (or any other bass and treble tone control system) to give a slightly more sophisticated three tone control circuit. The circuit is an active type which gives nominally unity voltage gain, and this type of circuit is very easy to fit into an audio system since it does not introduce problems of inadequate or excessive gain if it is added between (say) a preamplifier and a power amplifier which operate satisfactorily when directly coupled together. This is not the case with passive circuits which give losses of about 20dB, and some active circuits which give around 20dB of gain. The circuit provides a maximum boost of about 12dB at 100 Herts and 10 kilohertz, and similar level of maximum cut.

### The Circuit

Figure 15 shows the full circuit diagram of the Tone Controls. IC1a is a straight forward unity gain buffer stage which ensures

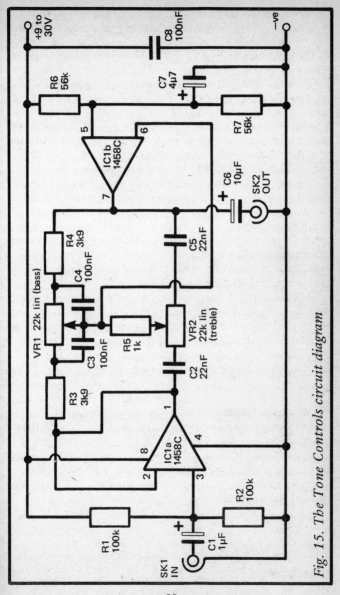

Fig. 15. The Tone Controls circuit diagram

29

that the tone control circuit is fed from a suitably low source impedance, and it also gives the circuit a reasonably high input impedance of about 50 kilohms.

The main tone control circuit is built around IC1b which is used as an inverting amplifier, and frequency selective negative feedback is used to provide the boost or cut in gain at high and low frequencies. VR2 is the treble control, and this works in conjunction with C2, C5 and R5. With the slider of VR2 towards C2 there is a relatively high impedance from the output of IC1b to its inverting input, and a low impedance from the output of IC1a to the inverting input of IC1b. These two impedances form a negative feedback network over IC1b and give the circuit a significant voltage gain of about 12dB. With the wiper of VR2 towards C5 there is a low impedance from the output of IC1b to its inverting input, and a comparative high impedance from the output of IC1a to the inverting input of IC1b. This gives a very large amount of negative feedback and the circuit consequently gives less than unity voltage gain with losses of around 12dB or so. However, this only occurs at high frequencies where C2 and C5 have an impedance which is very low in relation to the value of VR2. At middle and low frequencies these two capacitors have a very high impedance so that the two feedback impedances are virtually identical, and the setting of VR2 has very little effect. Thus the required boost and cut at treble frequencies is produced, with unity voltage gain at middle and bass frequencies. R5 is included to limit the maximum boost and cut at very high frequencies to a reasonable level.

The bass control circuit operates in a similar manner. VR1 controls the amount of feedback applied to IC1b, but only at low frequencies. At middle and high frequencies C3 and C4 have a very low impedance in relation to that of VR1 so that VR1 is effectively short circuited. R3 and R4 then act as the negative feedback network and give unity voltage gain as they are equal in value. A secondary function of R3 and R4 is to limit the maximum amount of cut and boost provided by the circuit at very low frequencies.

Any supply voltage from about 9 to 30 volts can be used to power the circuit, and the current consumption is about 2.5 milliamps.

## Construction

Figure 16 shows a suitable 0.1in. matrix stripboard layout for the Tone Controls, and this is based on a board measuring 24 holes by 17 copper strips. Construction of the board is quite simple, but be careful not to omit the four breaks in the copper strips (between IC1's two rows of pins) or the three link wires. Also make sure that the track connections to VR1 and VR2 are the right way round, so that clockwise adjustment produces boost, and counter clockwise adjustment gives cut.

The unit could be constructed as a self contained unit for use between two items of equipment, but in most cases it will probably be possible to build the controls as part of a larger project. In either case it will be necessary to make up two component boards for stereo operation, and dual gang potentiometers would then be used for the two VR1s and the two VR2s.

### Components for Tone Controls (Figure 15)

*Resistors,* all ¼ watt 5%

| | | | |
|---|---|---|---|
| R1 | 100k | R2 | 100k |
| R3 | 3k9 | R4 | 3k9 |
| R5 | 1k | R6 | 56k |
| R7 | 56k | | |
| VR1 | 22k lin. carbon potentiometer | | |
| VR2 | 22k lin. carbon potentiometer | | |

*Capacitors*

| | | | |
|---|---|---|---|
| C1 | 1$\mu$F 63V radial electrolytic | C2 | 22nF polyester |
| | | C4 | 100nF polyester |
| C3 | 100nF polyester | C6 | 10$\mu$F 25V axial electrolytic |
| C5 | 22nF polyester | | |
| C7 | 4$\mu$7 63V radial electrolytic | C8 | 100nF polyester |

*Semiconductor*
IC1     1458C

*Miscellaneous*
0.1in. matrix stripboard
Wire, sockets, control knobs, etc.

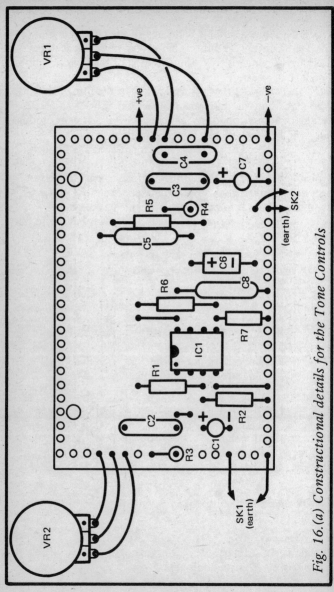

Fig. 16.(a) Constructional details for the Tone Controls

32

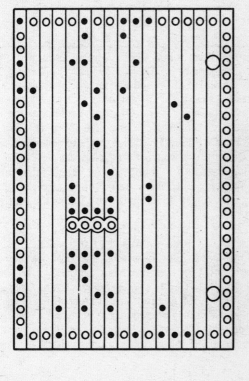

Fig. 16.(b) The underside of the component board

## Centre Tone Control

This tone control exerts maximum control at a frequency of about 900 Hertz, and provides about 12dB or so of boost and cut. This circuit is really only intended for use with convention: bass and treble controls (such as the circuit described in the previous section of this book), and is not of great value when used alone.

### *The Circuit*

The circuit as shown in Figure 17, is a gyrator type, and is much the same as the filters commonly used in graphic equalisers. Operation of the circuit is quite complex, but basically IC1a is u as an amplifier, and IC1b is used to simulate an inductor which gives the desired shaping of the amplifier's frequency response. The specified values for C4 and C5 give the filter a centre freque of approximately 900 hertz, as mentioned above, and this is abo optimum for use with most bass and treble tone control circuits However, if necessary the centre frequency can be altered by using a different value for C4 and C5, but bear in mind that changes in value produce an *inversely* proportional change in centre frequency (e.g. a doubling of value halves the centre frequency).

VR1 is the tone control potentiometer, and the circuit has approximately unity voltage gain and a flat frequency response with this control at a mid-way setting. The Q of the filter is not very high, and VR1 therefore has a significant effect on the gain of the circuit over quite a wide frequency range, but in this application this is not a disadvantage. In fact a high Q value with only a narrow range of frequencies being controlled would give unusable results in this application.

The current consumption of the circuit is about 2.5 milliamp

### *Construction*

The Centre Tone Control can be constructed on a piece of 0.1in. pitch stripboard using the component layout shown in Figure 18. This requires a board having 16 copper strips by 26 holes. Do not overlook the break in the copper strips which

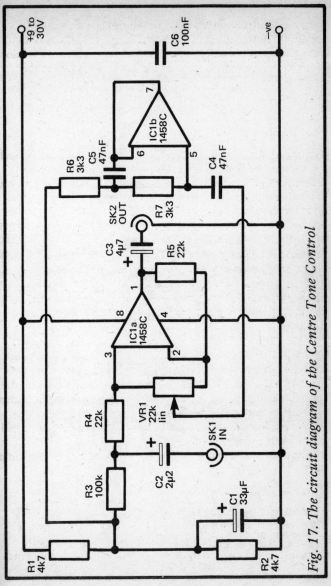

Fig. 17. The circuit diagram of the Centre Tone Control

35

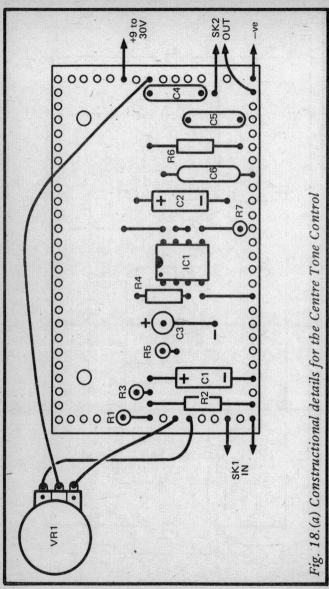

Fig. 18.(a) Constructional details for the Centre Tone Control

36

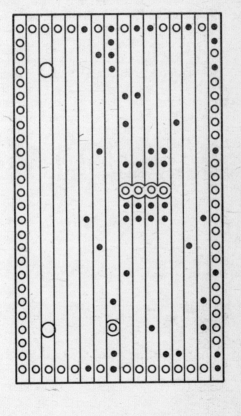

*Fig. 18. (b) The underside of the component board*

is required in addition to the four breaks between IC1's two rows of pins. Only three link wires are used. With VR1 wired as shown in Figure 18 clockwise adjustment provides boost and anticlockwise adjustment gives cut.

Like the tone control circuit described earlier, this circuit has nominally unity voltage gain and it should not therefore produce any problems if it is added into a signal path. The only point to bear in mind is that the unit should not be connected where it will process a very low signal level (less than about 50 millivolts RMS) or it may significantly degrade the signal to noise ratio of the audio system. Similarly, it should not have an input level which (in terms of peak-to-peak voltage) is more than about 4 volts below the supply voltage used, otherwise clipping and severe distortion will result. If the circuit is used to provide boost, then the maximum acceptable input signal is reduced by an amount which is equal to the boost provided by the circuit. Obviously a fairly high supply potential of around 15 to 30 volts is advisable if the unit is to be used to handle a high level signal. These points also apply to the bass and treble tone controls described earlier, incidentally.

*Components for Centre Tone Control (Figure 17)*

*Resistors,* all ¼ watt 5%

| | | | |
|----|------|-----|-----|
| R1 | 4k7 | R2 | 4k7 |
| R3 | 100k | R4 | 22k |
| R5 | 22k | R6 | 3k3 |
| R7 | 3k3 | | |
| VR1 | 22k lin. carbon potentiometer | | |

*Capacitors*

| | | | |
|----|-------------------------|----|-------------------|
| C1 | 33µF 16V axial electrolytic | C2 | 2µ2 50V axial electrolytic |
| C3 | 4µ7 50V axial or radial electrolytic | C4 | 47nF polyester |
| | | C6 | 100nF polyester |
| C5 | 47nF polyester | | |

*Semiconductor*

| | |
|-----|-------|
| IC1 | 1458C |

*Miscellaneous*
0.1in. matrix stripboard
Control knob
Connecting wire

## RIAA Preamplifier

The output from a magnetic or high output moving coil cartridge is normally in the 2.5 to 10 millivolt range, and a fairly sensitive preamplifier is therefore needed in order to match such a pick-up to a power amplifier (which is likely to need an input signal of a few hundred millivolts RMS). Although the output of magnetic and moving coil cartridges rises at 6dB per octave it is not necessary to include equalisation to counteract this since suitable equalisation is used during the recording process. However, equalisation is still needed since bass cut and treble boost are applied during the recording process, in addition to the tailoring of the frequency response that is used to counter-act the 6dB octave rise in output of the pick-up. The bass cut is used to prevent excessive groove modulations at low frequencies, and the treble boost (in conjunction with the treble cut during playback) provides a simple but effective form of noise reduction.

Figure 19 shows the required frequency response of an amplifier designed as a playback amplifier for normal RIAA standard recordings. Practical RIAA equalisation amplifiers usually deviate slightly from this ideal response even if factors such as component tolerances are not taken into account, but even using a simple equalisation network consisting of two resistor-capacitor pairs a maximum error of no more than about one or two dBs usually results, and this is perfectly satisfactory in practice.

### The Circuit

An NE5534 or NE5534A operational amplifier is used as the basis of this RIAA preamplifier, as can be seen from the circuit diagram which is given in Figure 20.

IC1 is used in the non-inverting mode, and the non-inverting input is biased to about half the supply potential by R1 and

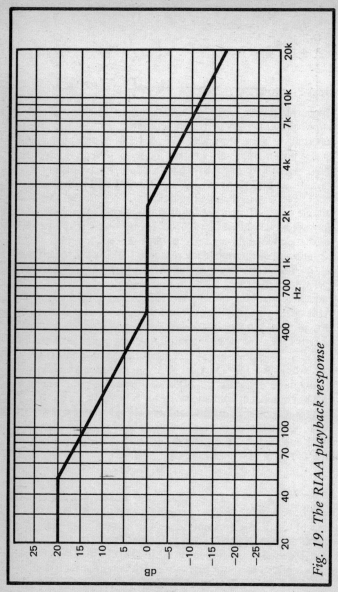

Fig. 19. The RIAA playback response

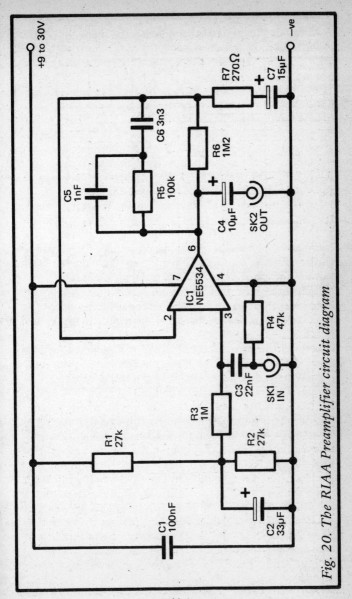

Fig. 20. The RIAA Preamplifier circuit diagram

41

R2, with R3 being used to couple this bias voltage to IC1. C2 filters out any hum or other noise on the supply lines and prevents this noise from being coupled to the input of the amplifier. The high value of R3 gives the circuit a high input impedance, but this is shunted to the required level of about 47k by R4. Some pick-ups have an optimum load impedance of 100k, and if the unit is to be used with a pick-up of this type R4 should be increased to 100k. The high input impedance of the amplifier enables a fairly low value component to be used in the C3 position without compromising the bass response of the circuit, and this is beneficial as it avoids having a large surge of current through the pick-up at switch-on as this component takes up its normal operating charge.

The required tailoring of the circuits frequency response is obtained using frequency selective negative feedback over IC1. At middle frequencies the gain of the circuit is largely determined by R5 and R7, but at lower frequencies C6 adds a significant impedance in series with R5 so that reduced negative feedback and the required increase in gain is produced. Similarly, at high frequencies the impedance of C5 becomes low in comparison to that of R5, and the shunting effect of C5 produces increased feedback and the required high frequency roll-off.

As the circuit provides over 50dB of voltage gain at middle audio frequencies it will give a high enough output voltage to drive any normal power amplifier even if it is used with a cartridge which only gives an output of around 2.5mV RMS. The circuit will operate from any supply voltage of between about 9 and 30 volts, but the use of a fairly high supply potential (about 20 to 30 volts) is recommended in order to give a reasonable overload margin. If the circuit is used with a high output pick-up and a supply voltage of only about 9 volts it is quite likely that at least slight overloading will occur.

The signal to noise ratio obtained depends on the output level and source impedance of the particular pick-up used, but the low noise level of the NE5534 plus the relatively low voltage gain of the circuit at high frequencies give excellent results in this respect with a typical signal to noise ratio of well over 70dB. The NE5534 also gives low levels of distortion.

A supply current of only about 4 milliamps is required by the circuit.

## Construction

The unit can be built as a self contained preamplifier, for use between a magnetic pick-up and a power amplifier which does not have a suitable built in preamplifier perhaps, or for use with a hi-fi amplifier which has a built-in RIAA preamplifier, but one which has a level of performance which leaves something to be desired. If constructed in this way the unit should be housed in a metal case and if a mains power supply is used it should be separated as far as possible from the preamplifier circuitry. The circuit has good ripple rejection and it is not essential to use a particularly well smoothed supply.

Of course, the unit can also be constructed as part of a larger project such as an integrated hi-fi amplifier or receiver. In either case the printed circuit layout shown in Figure 21 (component layout) and Figure 22 (track pattern) can be employed. This is for a mono unit, and for stereo operation it will be necessary to make up two boards, one for use in each stereo channel.

If, in use, the gain of the circuit seems to be excessive (which it is quite possible if a high output cartridge or sensitive power amplifier is used) the gain of the circuit can be reduced somewhat by making R7 higher in value.

## Components for RIAA Preamplifier (Figure 20)

*Resistors,* all ¼ watt 5%

| | | | |
|----|--------|----|------|
| R1 | 27k | R2 | 27k |
| R3 | 1M | R4 | 47k |
| R5 | 100k | R6 | 1M2 |
| R7 | 270 ohms | | |

*Capacitors*

| | | | |
|----|------------------|----|-------------------|
| C1 | 100nF polyester | C2 | 33μF 16V axial electrolytic |
| C3 | 22nF polyester | | |
| C5 | 1nF mylar | C4 | 10μF 25V axial electrolytic |
| C7 | 15μF 25V axial electrolytic | C6 | 3n3 mylar |

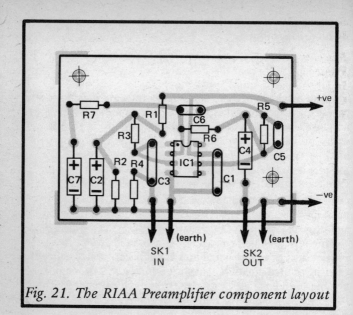

Fig. 21. The RIAA Preamplifier component layout

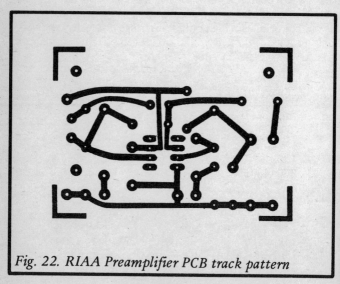

Fig. 22. RIAA Preamplifier PCB track pattern

44

*Semiconductor*
IC1     NE5534A

*Miscellaneous*
Printed circuit board
Input and output sockets (SK1 and SK2)
Case
Wire, etc.

## Chapter 2

## POWER AMPLIFIERS

In this chapter a number of power amplifier designs will be described ranging from simple low power integrated circuit based designs to high power MOSFET types. An 18 watt amplifier which operates from a 12 volt supply (for applications such as a car radio booster) is also included.

### 800mW Amplifier

For low power applications integrated circuit power amplifiers tend to give better results and reliability than discrete equivalent and are generally a little cheaper to construct as well. There are numerous audio power amplifier devices available, and these are all capable of a worthwhile level of performance. The integrated circuit used in this design is the ULN2283 (which is often just shown as the 2283 in retailers lists), and this device requires few discrete components to produce a complete amplifier circuit. It will work on a wide supply voltage range of 3 to 12 volts, and the output quality is more than adequate for a small power amplifier (where the loudspeaker used is normally the main limiting factor on output quality).

Figure 23 shows the circuit diagram of the 800mW audio power amplifier. Apart from the supply connections (including four pins which connect to the negative supply) there are only three other terminals on the ULN2283. One is the output, and this is coupled to the loudspeaker by way of DC blocking capacitor C3. Like most integrated circuit power amplifiers the ULN2283 has a class AB output stage.

Pin 1 of IC1 is the inverting input and an internal negative feedback circuit of the device connects to this input. This feedback network requires a discrete DC blocking capacitor, and in this circuit this component is C2. The feedback circuit gives the device a typical voltage gain of 43dB (about 140 times). The non-inverting input is pin 8, and this requires a bias resistance of about 100 kilohms or less to the negative supply rail. In this circuit volume control VR1 provides the required

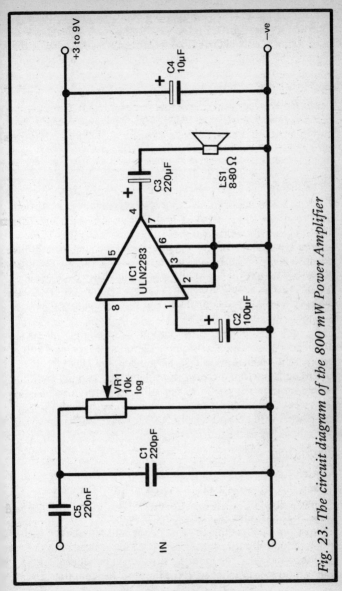

Fig. 23. The circuit diagram of the 800 mW Power Amplifier

47

biasing. C5 prevents DC inputs from being coupled to IC1 (and upsetting its biasing). C1 is used to filter out stray feedback at radio frequencies which could otherwise cause instability if the input of the amplifier was to be left open circuit, or if it is fed from a fairly high source impedance. C4 is a supply decoupling capacitor.

The output power of the circuit depends on the supply voltage and speaker impedance selected. Using a 9 volt supply and an 8 ohm loudspeaker an output power of about 800mW RMS can be achieved. Lower supply voltages and higher impedance loudspeakers give a correspondingly lower output power, with only about 170mW RMS being possible using a 4.5 volt supply and an 8 ohm impedance loudspeaker. The efficiency of the circuit inevitably reduces somewhat at lower supply voltages. In order to obtain a reasonable output power using a low supply voltage it is therefore necessary to use an 8 ohm loudspeaker and not a high impedance type. An output power of about 875mW can be achieved using a 12 volt supply and a 16 ohm impedance loudspeaker. Note though, that the use of a 12 volt supply and 8 ohm (or lower) impedance loudspeaker is not recommended, and that the supply potential must not exceed 12.5 volts.

The quiescent current consumption of the circuit is about 10 milliamps using a 6 volt supply, 12 milliamps with a 9 volt supply, or 17 milliamps using a 12 volt supply. However, the current consumption increases considerably at high output powers, and can rise to more than 100 milliamps. A large battery such as a PP9 type would therefore be needed if the unit is used with a 9 volt supply into an 8 ohm loudspeaker.

*Construction*

A suitable stripboard layout for this amplifier is given in Figure 24, and this is based on a 0.1in. pitch board which measures 15 holes by 14 copper strips. There are no link wires, but do not overlook the two breaks in the copper strips.

For some applications the gain of the unit may be too high, with an input of only about 20mV RMS being needed to produce maximum output. The input sensitivity can be reduced by adding a resistor in series with the input to the amplifier, and

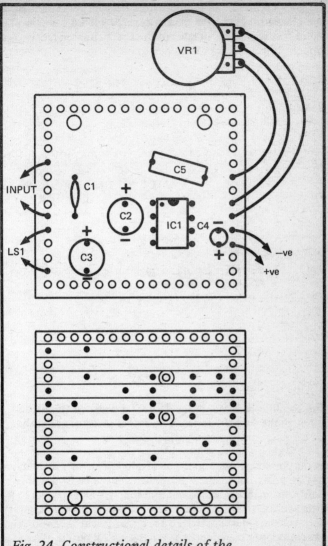

Fig. 24. Constructional details of the
800 mW Amplifier

as the circuit has an input impedance of about 10 kilohms a 10 kilohm resistor halves the sensitivity, a 20 kilohm component reduces sensitivity by a factor of three, a 30 kilohm resistor reduces it by a factor of four, and so on.

*Components for 800mW Amplifier (Figure 23)*

*Resistor*
VR1      10k log. carbon potentiometer

*Capacitors*

| | | | |
|---|---|---|---|
| C1 | 220pF ceramic plate | C2 | 100µF 10V radial |
| C3 | 220µF 10V radial | | electrolytic |
| | electrolytic | C4 | 10µF 25V radial |
| C5 | 220nF carbonate | | electrolytic |

*Semiconductor*
IC1      ULN2283

*Miscellaneous*
LS1      Loudspeaker having an impedance in the range 8 to 80 ohms
0.1in. matrix stripboard (15 holes by 14 strips)
Control knob
Wire, etc.

## 2 Watt Amplifier

This amplifier is based on the TBA820 integrated circuit, and although the TBA800 series of devices are far from new, they are very useful components which are probably as popular now as when they were first introduced. The TBA820 can provide an output power of up to 2 watts RMS using a 12 volt supply and an 8 ohm impedance loudspeaker. It can be used with higher impedance loudspeakers and supply voltages down to as little as 3 volts, but in either case the maximum output power is, of course, reduced. The TBA820 is excellent for use in battery powered equipment as it has a class B output stage which gives a quiescent current consumption of only about 4 milliamps (but bear in mind that the consumption can rise to as much as 250 milliamps or so when the amplifier is providing the full 2 watts RMS maximum output power).

## The Circuit

As can be seen from the circuit diagram of Figure 25, the TBA820 requires a few more discrete components than many audio amplifier ICs, but in certain respects some of these additional components provide greater versatility and improved performance. Components which do not fall into this category are C4 and C6 which are merely needed to prevent high frequency instability.

Pin 5 is the inverting input of IC1, and there is an internal 6 kilohm resistor between this input and the output of the device. This enables the voltage gain of the amplifier to be controlled by an external resistor and DC blocking capacitor, and the voltage gain is approximately equal to the value of the internal resistor divided by the value of the discrete resistor. This enables the gain of the amplifier to be adjusted over quite wide limits, and good stability is maintained within these limits. It is advisable not to make R1 less than about 22 ohms or the output quality may noticeably deteriorate, and a value of more than about 220 ohms might give poor stability. The specified value for R1 gives a voltage gain of just over 40dB (one hundred times).

VR1 is the volume control and is also used to bias the non-inverting input of IC1 to the negative supply rail. C1 provides DC blocking at the input of the amplifier. C3 decouples the supply to the preamplifier stages of IC1, and this helps to give the circuit good ripple rejection. This enables the circuit to be powered from a simple mains power supply without an excessive hum level being evident on the output, but for battery operation C3 will probably be of little or no help.

C5 and R2 are boostrapping components, and this technique helps to give the circuit good efficiency. It is especially useful if the circuit is run from a low voltage supply, and then provides a significant boost in output power. R2 forms part of the collector load for the driver transistor of IC1, and by coupling the output signal back to R2 via C5 the supply voltage to the driver stage is taken above the positive supply potential on

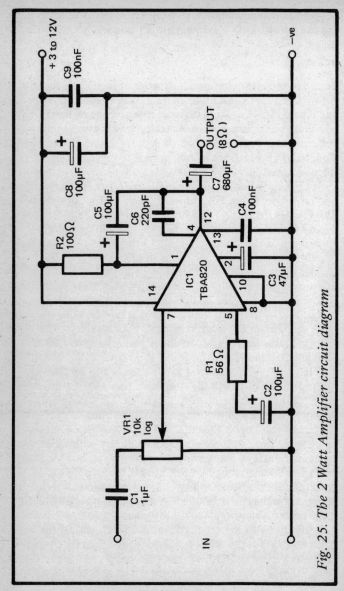

Fig. 25. The 2 Watt Amplifier circuit diagram

52

positive output half cycles. Normally the voltage drop through the output transistors of an amplifier limits the maximum output voltage to about one volt or more below the positive supply voltage, but the effective boost in the supply voltage to the driver stage provided by bootstrapping enables the output of the amplifier to achieve nearly the full supply potential.

Supply decoupling is provided by C8 and C9 while C7 is the output coupling capacitor.

## Construction

A suitable printed circuit design for this amplifier is provided in Figures 26 and 27. The component layout is quite compact and it is essential to use modern miniature capacitors if all the components are to be comfortably accommodated on the board.

The TBA820 has an unusual 14 pin quad-in-line (QIL) package which should plug into the printed circuit board without any difficulty. Make sure you obtain the TBA820 and not the TBA820M (which is basically the same device, but is in an 8 pin DIL package, and cannot be used in this circuit as a direct replacement for the TBA820).

Do not use the amplifier with a nominal supply voltage of more than 12 volts (16 volts is the maximum permissible supply voltage for the TBA820), or with a load impedance of less than 8 ohms. The TBA820 does not have thermal overload protection circuitry, but provided you observe the above limitations this should not be of any consequence. It does not have output short circuit protection either, and although short circuits across the output do not always result in the destruction of the device it is obviously advisable to be careful to avoid such overloads.

*Components for 2 Watt Amplifier (Figure 25)*

*Resistors,* all ¼ watt 5%

| | | | |
|---|---|---|---|
| R1 | 56 ohms | R2 | 100 ohms |
| VR1 | 10k log. carbon potentiometer | | |

*Capacitors*

| | | | |
|---|---|---|---|
| C1 | 1µF carbonate | C2 | 100µF 10V axial |
| C3 | 47µF 10V axial | | electrolytic |
| | electrolytic | C4 | 100nF polyester |

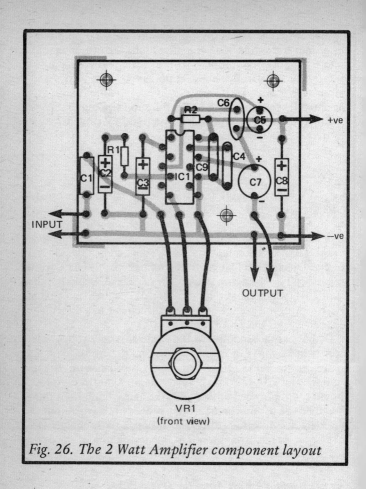

*Fig. 26. The 2 Watt Amplifier component layout*

| | | | |
|---|---|---|---|
| C5 | 100µF 10V radial electrolytic | C6 | 220pF ceramic plate |
| C7 | 680µF 10V radial electrolytic | C8 | 100µF 16V axial electrolytic |
| C9 | 100nF polyester | | |

*Semiconductor*
IC1    TBA820

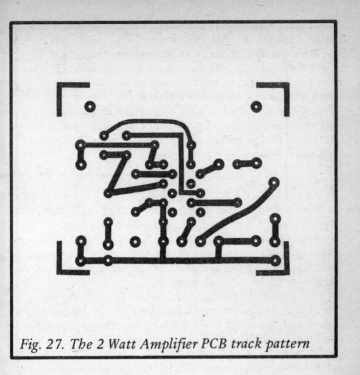

*Fig. 27. The 2 Watt Amplifier PCB track pattern*

*Miscellaneous*
Printed circuit board
Control knob
Wire, etc.


## 6 Watt Amplifier

This simple power amplifier design gives an output power of
about 6 watts RMS using a 24 volt supply and an 8 ohm
impedance loudspeaker. The input impedance of the circuit
is about 10 kilohms and an input level of around 225 millivolts
RMS is needed in order to produce full output. However, the
gain and input impedance of the circuit can both vary over

wide limits with suitable changes in component values, as will be explained in more detail later.

While the output quality of the unit is not in the true hi-fi class, the total harmonic distortion is typically under 0.1% at most output powers, and the quality of the amplifier is sufficient for applications such as record players, cassette players, etc. Due to the fairly high supply voltage required and the substantial current consumption of up to about 500 milliamps, it is not really feasable to operate the unit from a battery supply, and a mains power supply must be used.

## The Circuit

A TDA2030 integrated circuit is used as the basis of this amplifier, see Figure 28, and the TDA2030 is very much like an operational amplifier having a high power class A/B output stage. It has inverting and non-inverting inputs, but unlike most audio power amplifier devices it does not have any internal biasing or feedback components.

It is possible to use the TDA2030 with a single supply or dual balanced supplies, and it can operate in the inverting and non-inverting modes. In this circuit a single supply is employed and the TDA2030 is used as a non-inverting amplifier. The circuit is really just a straight forward operational amplifier style non-inverting circuit with R1, R2 and C3 being used to effectively supply a central supply rail. The non-inverting input is biased to this by R3, and C4 provides DC blocking at the input of the amplifier. VR1 is the volume control.

R4 and R5 are the negative feedback loop and these set the closed loop voltage gain of the amplifier at approximately 30 times. C5 provides DC blocking so that R4 is effectively cut out of circuit at DC, giving unity voltage gain from the non-inverting input to the output. Thus, by biasing the non-inverting input of IC1 to half the supply potential the output is also biased to this voltage. This optimises the output power that can be achieved prior to the onset of clipping and severe distortion.

C6 is the output coupling capacitor, and C1 plus C2 are supply decoupling components. D1 and D2 are protection diodes. The quiescent current consumption of the circuit is typically 40 milliamps incidentally.

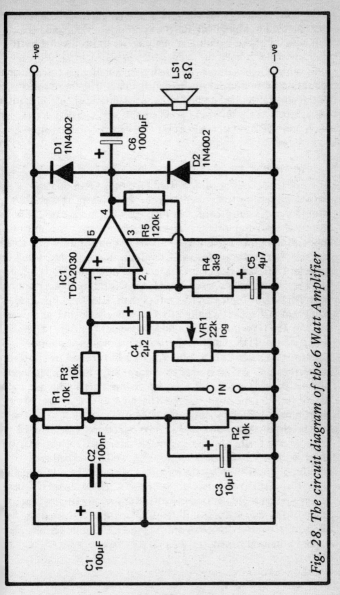

Fig. 28. The circuit diagram of the 6 Watt Amplifier

57

Within reason the voltage gain of the amplifier can be set at any desired level by giving R5 the appropriate value, and the voltage gain of the circuit is roughly equal to R5 divided by R4. It is advisable to keep the value of R5 between about 39k and 390k since there is otherwise a risk of instability or a significant reduction in the output quality of the unit. The input impedanc of the circuit can be boosted by increasing the values of R3 and VR1, but in the interests of good stability it is advisable to regar 100k and 220k respectively as the highest acceptable values.

## Construction

The 6 Watt Amplifier can be assembled on a 0.1in. matrix stripboard having 13 copper strips by 29 holes using the component layout provided in Figure 29. There are no breaks in any of the copper strips. The electrolytic capacitors must be modern miniature types if they are to fit comfortably into this layout. The leadout wires of IC1 will need to be formed slightly in order to fit this device into place, and this integrated circuit has a rather unusual case style which looks rather like a plastic power transistor but with five rather than three leadout wires. Note that IC1 must be bolted to a large heatsink such as a ready-made type rated at around 4.5 degrees Centigrade per watt. As the TDA2030 has thermal shutdown protection circuits it will probably not be damaged if it should be allowed to overheat. It would simply shut down until the temperature of the device dropped to a satisfactory level, after which it would function normally again. The TDA2030 also has output short circuit protection circuits incidentally.

The circuit has good supply ripple rejection (which can be boosted still further by increasing the value of C3 if necessary), and it is therefore unnecessary to use a well smoothed and stabilised power supply. An important point to bear in mind though is that the supply voltage under quiescent loading will be very much higher than the loaded supply potential if a non-stabilised supply is used, and the supply voltage must not be allowed to exceed 36 volts (which is the maximum permissible supply potential for the TDA2030).

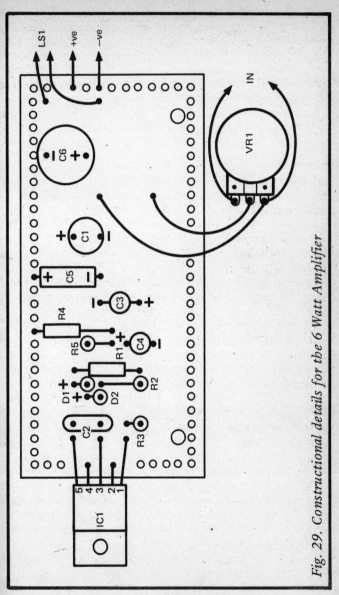

Fig. 29. Constructional details for the 6 Watt Amplifier

59

*Components for 6 Watt Amplifier (Figure 28)*

*Resistors,* all ¼ watt 5%

| | | | |
|---|---|---|---|
| R1 | 10k | R2 | 10k |
| R3 | 10k | R4 | 3k9 |
| R5 | 120k | | |
| VR1 | 22k log. carbon potentiometer | | |

*Capacitors*

| | | | |
|---|---|---|---|
| C1 | 100µF 40V radial electrolytic | C2 | 100nF polyester |
| | | C4 | 2µ2 50V radial electrolytic |
| C3 | 10µF 25V radial electrolytic | C6 | 1000µF 25V radial electrolytic |
| C5 | 4µ7 50V axial electrolytic | | |

*Semiconductors*

| | | | |
|---|---|---|---|
| IC1 | TDA2030 | | |
| D1 | 1N4002 | D2 | 1N4002 |

*Miscellaneous*

0.1in. matrix stripboard
Loudspeaker rated at 5 watts or more and an impedance of 8 ohms
Control knob
Wire, etc.


## 18 Watt Bridge Amplifier

It is sometimes necessary to operate audio equipment from a supply voltage of only about 12 volts, and in-car-entertainment equipment and equipment for use in small craft are a couple of obvious examples of this. A drawback of a low supply voltage is that the maximum peak to peak output voltage swing that can be achieved (assuming a normal transformerless output stage is used) can be no more than the supply voltage, and in practice is likely to be around one to four volts less depending on the particular type of output stage employed.

Using normal 4 or 8 ohm impedance loudspeakers and a 12 volt supply this gives maximum output powers of about 4.5 watts RMS and 2.25 watts RMS respectively. This actually enables quite a reasonable volume level to be obtained, but obviously under some circumstances (such as in a noisy vehicle) greater output power might be advantageous.

A simple way of obtaining a higher output power is to use a bridge amplifier, and Figure 30 outlines the basic arrangement of this form of amplifier. A bridge amplifier actually uses two power amplifiers with the loudspeaker connected between the outputs of the stages of amplification. One amplifier (amplifier 1 in this case) is fed with the input signal and is really just a straight forward non-inverting power amplifer. The second amplifier is a unity voltage gain inverting type and its input is fed from the output of amplifier 1.

Under quiescent conditions the outputs of both amplifier stages are at about half the supply voltage and there is no significant voltage developed across the loudspeaker. If the output of amplifier 1 goes positive, the output of amplifier 2 goes negative by an identical amount. Similarly, if the output of amplifier 1 goes negative, the output of amplifier 2 goes positive by an identical amount. Thus, if the amplifier is fully driven the outputs of the amplifiers reach virtually the full supply potentials on signal peaks, but they are out-of-phase and therefore one output is fully negative while the other is fully positive. Effectively the loudspeaker is first connected across the supply lines with one polarity, and then with the opposite polarity, and so on, giving a peak to peak output voltage equal to almost double the supply potential. Since doubling the output voltage also doubles the output current (and power is equal to current multiplied by voltage), this gives a fourfold increase in output power in comparison to an ordinary amplifier. In other words using a 12 volt supply and 4 or 8 ohm impedance loudspeakers gives maximum output powers of up to about 18 watts RMS and 9 watts RMS respectively.

*The Circuit*

There are audio power ICs which are specifically designed for use in 12 volt bridge amplifier circuits, and it is also possible to use a pair of audio power amplifiers such as a couple of TDA2030 ICs. This circuit is based on an HA1388 integrated

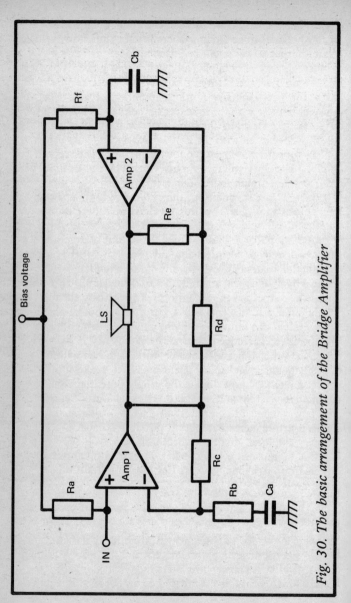

Fig. 30. The basic arrangement of the Bridge Amplifier

circuit which contains both the amplifiers needed to produce a 12 volt bridge amplifier, and this device has been chosen primarily because it is relatively inexpensive and seems to be readily available from a number of component retailers. It also gives excellent performance. The circuit diagram of the 18 Watt Bridge Amplifier is shown in Figure 31.

R1 and R2 form an attenuator at the input of the unit, but these are only needed if the unit is used as a booster amplifier for use with a car radio or cassette player. In this application only a very modest amount of voltage gain is needed and the voltage gain of about 40dB (100 times) provided by IC1 would obviously be excessive. If the unit is used in other applications where the full voltage gain is required R2 should be omitted and R1 should be replaced with a link wire.

The HA1388 has internal bias and negative feedback circuits, and the only discrete components these require are four DC blocking capacitors (C3 to C6). C7 and C8 are needed to aid good stability. C9 and C10 are bootstrapping capacitors which help to optimise the efficiency and output power of the circuit. No coupling capacitor is needed in series with the loudspeaker since there is no more than a few millivolts developed across this component under quiescent conditions. C1 is a supply decoupling capacitor and this has a fairly high value in order to additionally provide suppression of any severe noise spikes which may be present on the supply.

*Construction*

A suitable 0.1 inch pitch stripboard component layout for the Bridge Amplifier is provided in Figure 32. Be careful not to omit the single link wire along side IC1. IC1 has an unusual 12 pin package which has the 12 pins in a single row. As the spacing of the pins is 0.1 inches this device obviously plugs into the stripboard without difficulty.

IC1 must be bolted to a large heatsink and this should preferably be rated at only about 3 degrees Centigrade per watt or less. If the unit is housed in a metal case it may well be possible to use this as the heatsink. It is acceptable for the heat-tab of IC1 to connect to the negative supply rail, and it will probably be unnecessary to insulate IC1 from the heatsink or

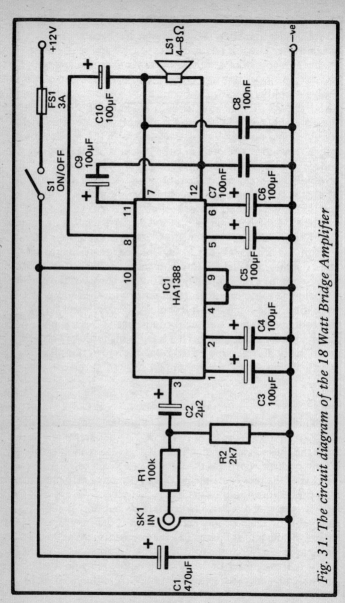

Fig. 31. The circuit diagram of the 18 Watt Bridge Amplifier

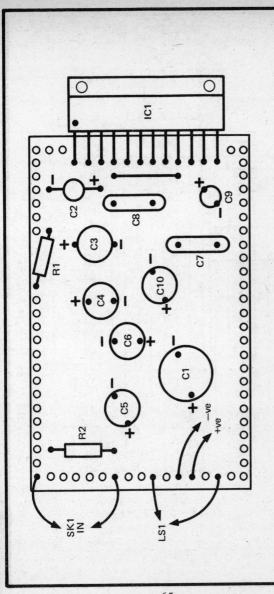

Fig. 32.(a) Constructional details for the 18W Bridge Amplifier.

65

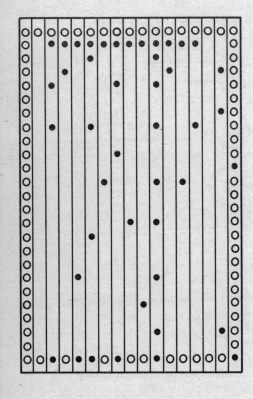

*Fig. 32. (b) The underside of the component board.*

case. However, it must not connect to the positive supply rail and insulation would therefore be needed in a positive earth set-up.

FS1 is not shown in Figure 32, but this component is an in-line type.

Note that neither loudspeaker lead is at earth potential, and neither of these leads should be permitted to short circuit to earth (which would blow FS1 but would probably not do any other damage to the unit).

*Components for 18 Watt Bridge Amplifier (Figure 31)*

*Resistors,* both ¼ watt 5%

| | | | |
|---|---|---|---|
| R1 | 100k | R2 | 2k7 |

*Capacitors*

| | | | |
|---|---|---|---|
| C1 | 470µF 16V radial electrolytic | C2 | 2µ2 50V radial electrolytic |
| C3 | 100µF 10V radial electrolytic | C4 | 100µF 10V radial electrolytic |
| C5 | 100µF 10V radial electrolytic | C6 | 100µF 10V radial electrolytic |
| C7 | 100nF polyester | C8 | 100nF polyester |
| C9 | 100µF 10V radial electrolytic | C10 | 100µF 10V radial electrolytic |

*Semiconductor*

| | |
|---|---|
| IC1 | HA1388 |

*Miscellaneous*

| | |
|---|---|
| S1 | SPST toggle switch |
| FS1 | 3 amp in-line fuse holder and fuse |
| SK1 | 3.5mm jack |
| LS1 | 4 or 8 ohm, 10 or 20 watts RMS loudspeaker |

0.1in. matrix stripboard
Case
Wire, etc.

## Auto Switching Unit

This unit is designed as an add-on for the previous project, and is used when the Bridge Amplifier is used as a booster amplifier for a car radio or cassette unit. The Auto Switch Unit simply switches on the booster amplifier when the radio or cassette unit is switched on, and switches the booster off again when the radio or cassette unit is turned off. This is a useful feature since it enables the unit to be mounted at any convenient point in the car, and it does not have to be positioned where it can be turned on and off easily.

### The Circuit

Figure 33 shows the circuit diagram of the Auto Switching Unit. The input signal is coupled to Tr1 which is used as a low gain common emitter amplifier. R1 is used to reduce the input impedance of the circuit and this helps to avoid spurious operation of the unit by electrical noise.

The output of Tr1 is smoothed and rectified by C3, D1 and D2, and the resultant DC bias (in the presence of an input signal from the radio or cassette unit) is used to bias the Darlington Pair (Tr2 and Tr3) into conduction. These switch on relay RLA1 and a set of normally open relay contacts are used to connect power to the booster amplifier. Of course, when the radio or cassette unit is switched off the input signal ceases, the charge on C3 decays after a few seconds, causing RLA1 and the booster amplifier to be switched off.

### Construction

A suitable 0.1 inch matrix stripboard layout for the Auto Switching Unit is shown in Figure 34. The relay is not mounted on the component board, although the board could obviously be made larger in order to accommodate it if desired. The relay used in the prototype has a 12 volt 306 ohm coil plus 8 amp changeover contacts. However, any relay having a 12 volt coil, a coil resistance of about 300 ohms or more, and at least one set of normally open contacts of adequate rating should be suitable.

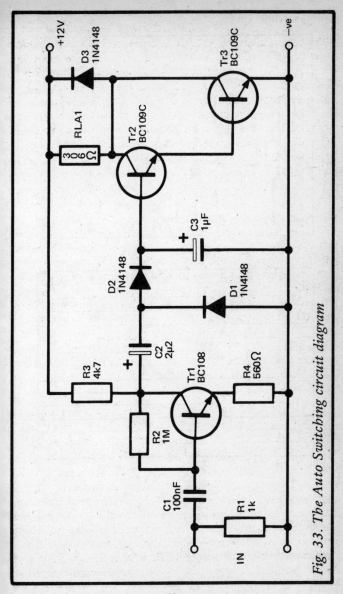

Fig. 33. The Auto Switching circuit diagram

69

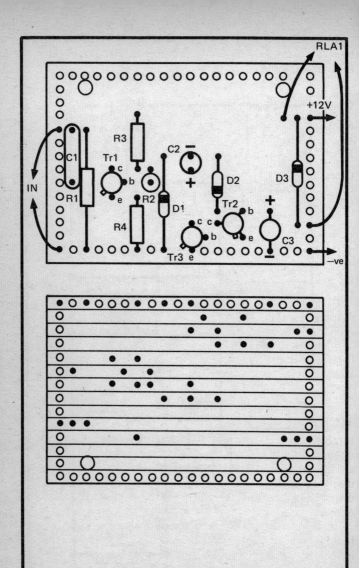

Fig. 34. Constructional details of the
Auto Switching circuit

Note that power for the Audo Switching Unit should not be obtained via the relay contacts, but must be taken direct from the car supply.

*Components for Auto-Switching Unit (Figure 33)*

*Resistors,* all ¼ watt 5%

| | | | |
|---|---|---|---|
| R1 | 1k | R2 | 1M |
| R3 | 4k7 | R4 | 560 ohms |

*Capacitors*

| | | | |
|---|---|---|---|
| C1 | 100nF polyester | C2 | 2μ2 50V radial electrolytic |
| C3 | 1μF 50V radial electrolytic | | |

*Semiconductors*

| | | | |
|---|---|---|---|
| Tr1 | BC108 | Tr2 | BC109C |
| Tr3 | BC109C | | |
| D1 | 1N4148 | D2 | 1N4148 |
| D3 | 1N4148 | | |

*Miscellaneous*

RLA1    306 ohm 12 volt coil with 8 amp changeover contacts
           (or similar)
0.1in. matrix stripboard
Wire, etc.


## 32W + 32W MOSFET Amplifier

Integrated circuits are commonly used in power amplifiers of up to about 10 or 20 watts RMS in output power, but there are few types capable of providing higher output powers even if used in a bridge circuit, and it generally is better to use a discrete design for output powers of around 25 watts RMS or more.

Higher power audio amplifiers used to almost invariably be based on bipolar transistors, including bipolar power devices in the output stage. However, various types of power field effect device, especially power MOSFETs, have become increasingly popular in recent times. Although power MOSFETs tend to be associated with very high power and high qualtiy designs, they are in fact perfectly practical for medium and high power applications, and where super hi-fi performance is not essential. The advantages of power MOSFETs do not significantly diminish in medium and high power applications.

## Bipolar Drawbacks

While bipolar devices can be used in high performance audio power amplifiers, they do have shortcomings which have resulted in the development of superior devices such as power MOSFETs. Probably the best known drawback of bipolar devices in Class B output stages is the effect known as thermal runaway. Bipolar devices have a positive temperature coefficient and it is this that leads to thermal runaway and the possible destruction of the output transistors.

Figure 35(a) shows the basic arrangement of a conventional Class B driver and output stage, using Tr1 as a common emitter driver stage and Tr2 plus Tr3 as the complementary emitter follower output stage. The purpose of the output stage is to give current amplification (the voltage gain being only about unity) so that the circuit can provide the high output currents needed to drive a loudspeaker at high volume. Tr2 supplies the output current during positive going output excursions while Tr3 provides the output current during negative output half cycles.

The main collector load for the driver transistor is formed by a constant current source, and this gives improved linearity in comparison to results obtained using a straight forward load resistor. This is due to the variations in gain (and consequent distortion) that result when a transistor operates over a wide range of collector currents. Using a load resistor in a common emitter stage which has a large output voltage swing inevitably results in a very wide collector current range and substantial distortion. The use of a constant current load does not totally eliminate distortion since the collector voltage does obviously vary, and the gain of a transistor is to a certain extent dependent on collector voltage. However, as changes in gain due to variations in collector voltage are relatively small, low distortion levels of only a fraction of one percent can be readily achieved.

The bias circuit between the bases of the output transistors

72

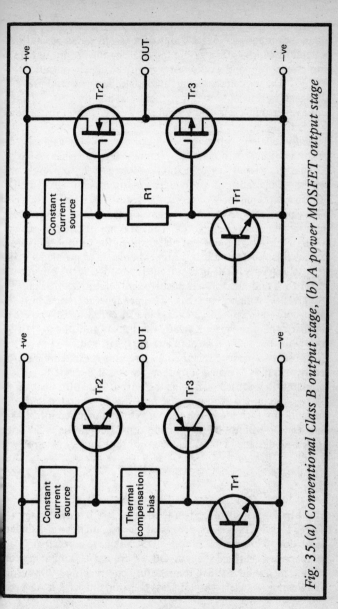

*Fig. 35.(a) Conventional Class B output stage, (b) A power MOSFET output stage*

is needed to bring the output transistors to the point where they are just conducting. If this is not done, small variations in the collector voltage of Tr1 would fail to bring the output devices into conduction and would not give any change in output voltage! Higher voltage swings at Tr1's collector would give a change in output potential, but the initial and final part of each half cycle would be missing, giving severe "crossover distortion" as it is termed.

Unfortunately, bringing the output devices to the threshold of conduction does not totally eliminate crossover distrotion because the output devices exhibit comparatively low levels of gain when operating at low collector currents. This gives a mild but unacceptable form of crossover distortion. Negative feedback can be used to combat crossover distortion of course, but in order to obtain really good results it is nevertheless necessary to use a fairly high quiescent bias through the output transistors

It is this substantial bias current that leads to problems with thermal runaway. The bias current tends to heat the output transistors, and due to their positive temperature coefficient this gives a rise in bias current. This produces increased heat and a consequent further increase in bias current. This positive feedback therefore gives a steady rise in bias until the output transistors become overheated and are destroyed.

In order to prevent this the bias circuit is made temperature sensitive, and is designed to reduce the bias if increased temperature is sensed. Thus, as the output transistor heat up the bias circuit is affected by the heat that is generated and prevents any increase in the bias current. In practice the bias stabilisation will not be perfect and some fluctuation will occur, but a well designed circuit will have more than adequate bias stability.

*Power MOSFETs*

Like bipolar transistors, when used in a Class B output stage power MOSFETs require a forward bias to minimise crossover distortion. However, as power MOSFETs have a negative temperature coefficient at currents of around 100 milliamps or more (and a mild positive temperature coefficient at low curren it is possible to use a simpler Class B driver and output stage, as shown in Figure 35(b). The temperature stabilised bias circuit can be replaced with a resistor since the temperature characteristics of power MOSFETs gives built in stabilisation of the bias current at about 100 milliamps (which is about the optimum bias current).

Another problem encountered with bipolar power devices is that of relatively low current gains of typically only around 20 to 50. This is inadequate for medium and high power amplifiers since it would require an excessively powerful driver stage. The normal way around this problem is to use Darlington Pairs or some similar arrangement to give a sufficiently high current gain to permit the use of a low power driver stage.

Power MOSFETs, like all FET devices, are voltage rather than current operated. The input impedance of power MOSFET devices is so high that no significant input current is drawn at low operating frequencies, but at high operating frequencies the input impedance is much lower due to the rather high input capacitance of around 500 picofarads. Despite this input capacitance an operating current of only about 10 milliamps through the driver stage is sufficient, even though the peak output current could be as much as a thousand times this figure.

A further drawback of bipolar power devices is their relatively slow switching time. This can produce a number of problems, including slewing induced distortion. This is where a strong high frequency signal may demand a change in output voltage of (say) 2 volts per microsecond, whereas the output stage might have a slew rate of perhaps just one volt per microsecond, obviously the output will be unable to give a faithful reproduction of the input signal and distortion inevitably results. An inadequate slew rate can also give an amplifier a poor power bandwidth, with the maximum available output power falling considerably at high audio frequencies.

A further problem is the phase lag which occurs through the output stage at high frequencies, and which can result in the feedback through the negative feedback network becoming positive rather than negative at very high frequencies. If the amplifier has sufficient gain at these frequencies the amplifier will oscillate, and instability will still be evident even if the gain of the circuit is not quite sufficient to produce oscillation.

This can be overcome by including components to roll-off

the high frequency response of the circuit, and by including phase compensation components. This reduces the performance of the amplifier at high audio frequencies though.

Power MOSFETs have a switching time that is typically about 50 to 100 times faster than a bipolar power transistor, and problems with poor high frequency performance are thus largely overcome by the use of these devices. It is in fact possible to produce designs which have no frequency or phase compensation components but still possess good stability, and have a level of performance which is maintained to frequencies well beyond the upper audio limit.

Another problem encountered with bipolar power transistors is that of secondary breakdown. This is a sort of localised therma runaway which produces a "hot spot" on the chip with a consequ short circuit between the collector and emitter terminals. This has to be avoided by only operating the transistor within certain combinations of collector current and voltage. In audio amplifier circuits this often means that the output transistors are operated well within their thermal limitations, and the maximum output power available from a given set of output transistors is often far less than their maximum dissipation figures would suggest.

Due to their negative temperature coefficient at high drain currents power MOSFETs do not suffer from secondary breakdov and the maximum drain current and drain voltage combinations that can be used are virtually only limited by the thermal dissipation capabilities of the devices. They are therefore eminently suitable for use in high power audio amplifiers.

## MOSFET Disadvantages

While MOSFET power devices are not without drawbacks, these are relatively few and minor. Originally they were very much more expensive than bipolar transistors of comparable power rating, but the price difference is very much smaller these days. When one takes into account the fact that the use of power MOSFETs allows more simple circuitry to be used with a consequent indirect saving in cost, it is probable that bipolar transistors no longer have a significant cost advantage.

Power MOSFETs tend to have higher open loop distortion

76

than bipolar devices, but the high gain and fast switching speed of power MOSFETs enables a high level of negative feedback to be used over the entire audio band, giving unsurpassed closed loop distortion performance.

Another drawback is that power MOSFETs tend to be rather less efficient than bipolar devices when used in conventional Class B output stages. This is simply because a high power emitter follower stage produces a voltage drop of up to about one volt or so between the input and output, whereas there is a drop of a few volts from the input to the output of a source follower stage. There is no easy way around this problem, but a slight reduction in efficiency is not really a major drawback anyway.

*Practical Circuit*

Figure 36 shows the circuit diagram of a practical 32 watt plus 32 watt power MOSFET amplifier, and apart from the use of MOSFETs in the output stage this is basically a quite conventional design.

Tr1 is a common emitter input stage, and is direct coupled to common emitter driver stage Tr3. These two stages provide all the amplifier's voltage gain, and have a very high combined gain. Tr2 and its associated components form a straight forward constant current generator having a nominal output current of 10 milliamps, and this forms the main collector load for Tr3. R10 is used to set the appropriate quiescent bias current through the output transistors, and as explained earlier, the thermal stabilisation of the bias current is not achieved in the bias circuit, but is instead provided by the output devices themselves.

R8 provides almost 100% negative feedback from the output of the amplifier to the emitter of Tr1, giving the circuit only about unity voltage gain at DC. R1, R2 and R4 are used as a potential divider which biases the input of the amplifier, and therefore the output as well, to approximately half the supply voltage. This permits the maximum possible output level prior to clipping and the commencement of serious distortion. R1 and C2 form a smoothing circuit which prevents hum and other noise on the supply lines from being coupled to the input of the amplifier through the bias circuit.

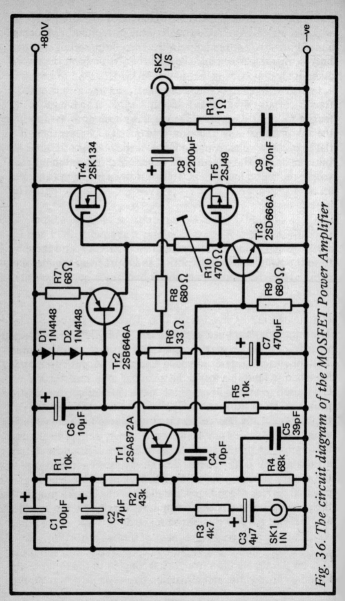

*Fig. 36. The circuit diagram of the MOSFET Power Amplifier*

78

R3 and C5 form an RF filter which helps to avoid problems with RF signals breaking through to the output and producing audible signals. C4 also helps in this respect by rolling-off the high frequency response of the amplifier, well above the upper audio limit.

In order to give the amplifier a useful voltage gain at audio frequencies it is necessary to decouple some of the negative feedback. C7 is the decoupling capacitor and R6 is used to limit the amount of feedback that is removed. The voltage gain of the circuit is roughly equal to R8 divided by R6, or about 20 times (26dB) with the specified values. The maximum output voltage of the amplifier is 16 volts RMS, and this gives an input sensitivity of approximately 777mV RMS for full output. The input impedance is over 20k.

C3 and C8 are the input and output coupling capacitors respectively while C1 provides supply decoupling. R11 and C9 are the only components required to aid stability, and these form the familiar Zobel network that is normally included across the output of semiconductor power amplifiers.

### Performance

The prototype amplifier seems to work extremely well, especially when one takes into account the relative simplicity of the unit. The circuit will comfortably give 32 watts RMS into an 8 ohm load, and the total harmonic distortion is only about 0.05% or less for any power level up to this figure. Measurements on the prototype were only made at 1kHz, but the open loop gain of the circuit is virtually constant over the audio frequency range, and the distortion performance should be as well. The closed loop frequency response of the circuit has −2dB points at approximately 20Hz and 22kHz. The signal to noise ratio of the circuit (unweighted) is in excess of 80dB, although in practice there is likely to be a small amount of mains hum from the power supply to add to the noise generated by the amplifier and this figure may not quite be realised.

### Power Supply

Figure 37 shows the circuit diagram of a suitable power supply

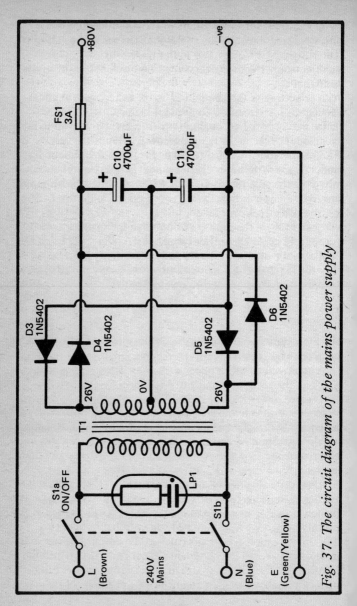

*Fig. 37. The circuit diagram of the mains power supply*

for the 32 watt plus 32 watt MOSFET amplifier, and this is sufficient to power a mono or a stereo version of the amplifier. The circuit is effectively two push-pull rectifier and smoothing circuits having their outputs connected in series to give a total output voltage equal to double the potential given by a single rectifier and smoothing circuit. D4, D6 and C10 form one section of the unit while the other is formed by D3, D5 and C11. These each give a little under 40 volts under no load, and a combined unloaded output potential of just under 80 volts. This drops to about 77 volts when loaded by a stereo amplifier under quiescent conditions, and to only about 60 volts or so when powering a stereo amplifier with both channels being run at high power.

S1 is the on/off switch and LP1 is the on/off indicator. It is essential that the latter is a type having a built-in series resistor for use on the 240 volt U.K. mains supply.

The mains transformer used in the prototype has a rating of $26 - 0 - 26$ volts at 3.5 amps, but it is not essential to use a component having precisely these ratings. A $25 - 0 - 25$ volt type rated at about 4 amps or more should be equally suitable. Do not use a type having a secondary voltage rating of more than 26 volts as this could result in the unloaded or quiescent loaded supply voltage being higher than the 40 volt rating of smoothing capacitors C10 and C11.

## Construction

A suitable printed circuit board design for the 32 watt MOSFET amplifier is shown in Figure 38 (the component layout) and Figure 39 (the track pattern). This is for a single amplifier and obviously two boards must be constructed if a stereo amplifier is required.

The output transistors are not mounted on the board, but are fitted on a large heatsink, and a "Redpoint" type 4Y heatsink (which is a 4.5 degree Centigrade per watt type) was used in the prototype. This can be obtained ready drilled to take two TO—3 style power transistors (such as the output devices used in this design) or it can be obtained undrilled. If you drill the heatsinks yourself a TO—3 size mica insulating washer can be used as a template when marking out the positions of the

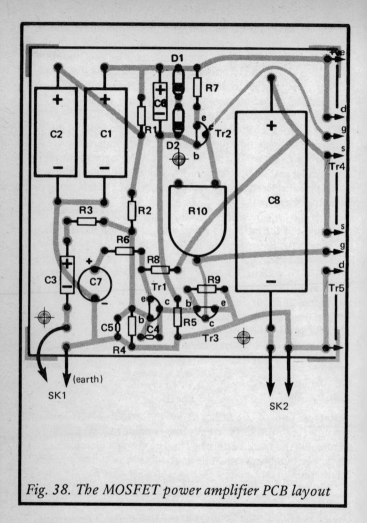

*Fig. 38. The MOSFET power amplifier PCB layout*

mounting holes. It is not essential to insulate the transistors from the heatsink since the sources of the transistors connect to their metal cases, and the sources of the transistors must connect to each other anyway. If they are not insulated from the heatsink it is clearly necessary to prevent the heatsinks from

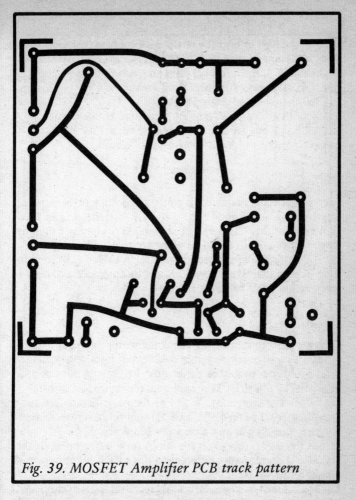

*Fig. 39. MOSFET Amplifier PCB track pattern*

coming into electrical contact with other parts of the circuit, and in a stereo circuit the separate heatsinks for the two amplifiers must not be allowed to come into electrical contact with one another.

It is important to use quite short leads of no more than about 50mm in length to connect the output transistors to the printed circuit board, and this is particularly important in the case of the leads which connect to the gate terminals of the output devices. Due to the high gain of the power MOSFETs at high frequencies long leads could result in poor stability or even RF oscillation and damage to the output transistors. However, in practice there should be no difficulty in arranging the layout of the unit so that these leads are suitably short.

Note that C9 and R11 are not mounted on the printed circuit board but are simply wired in series across the output socket. A screened input cable should be used.

*Power Supply Construction*

The power supply circuitry is constructed using point to point style wiring, as shown in Figure 40. This is quite straight forward but assumes that C10 and C11 are both types having a dummy tag. If they are not it will be necessary to use a tagstrip to provide a couple of connection points. A soldertag is fitted to one of the mounting bolts of T1, and this provides a chassis connection point for the mains earth lead.

*Adjustment*

It is essential to thoroughly check the wiring before switching the unit on since wiring errors could result in expensive damage, and could conceivably be dangerous. Before switching on it is essential to adjust R10 for minimum resistance (set in a fully anticlockwise direction). With FS1 temporarily removed and a multimeter set to read 500mA FSD connected across the fuseholder, a reading of approximately 20mA should be obtained when the unit is turned on (or 40mA for a stereo unit). If the reading is considerably different to this switch off at once and recheck the wiring.

If all is well, advance R10 to increase the meter reading to about 100mA. For a stereo unit R10 in one channel should be adjusted to bring the current consumption up to 120mA, after which R10 in the second channel should be adjusted to raise the current consumption to 200mA. The amplifier is then ready for use.

Be careful not to touch any of the mains connections when

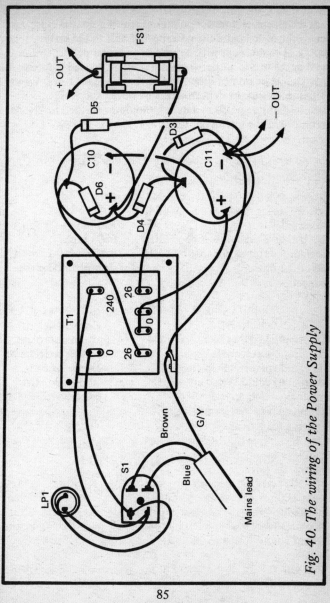

Fig. 40. The wiring of the Power Supply

making adjustments and measurements on the unit, and exposed wiring or connections at the mains potential must be well insulated before connecting the unit to the mains supply. Of course, as with any mains powered project the unit must be housed in a case which can only be opened with the aid of a screwdriver or other tool so that there is no easy way to gain access to the dangerous mains wiring and accidents are avoided. Any exposed metalwork should be earthed to the mains earth lead in the interest of safety.

*Components for 32 Watt MOSFET Amplifier (Figure 36)*

*Resistors,* all ¼ watt 5% except R10

| | | | |
|---|---|---|---|
| R1 | 10k | R2 | 43k |
| R3 | 4k7 | R4 | 68k |
| R5 | 10k | R6 | 33 ohms |
| R7 | 68 ohms | R8 | 680 ohms |
| R9 | 680 ohms | R10 | 470 ohms 0.25 watt horizontal preset |
| R11 | 1 ohm | | |

*Capacitors*

| | | | |
|---|---|---|---|
| C1 | 100µF 100V axial electrolytic | C2 | 47µF 100V axial electrolytic |
| C3 | 4µ7 63V axial electrolytic | C4 | 10pF ceramic plate |
| C5 | 39pF ceramic plate | C6 | 10µF 25V axial electrolytic |
| C7 | 470µF 63V radial electrolytic | C8 | 2200µF 63V axial electrolytic |
| C9 | 470nF polyester | | |

*Semiconductors*

| | | | |
|---|---|---|---|
| Tr1 | 2SA872A | Tr2 | 2SB646A |
| Tr3 | 2SD666A | Tr4 | 2SK134 |
| Tr5 | 2SJ49 | | |
| D1 | 1N4148 | D2 | 1N4148 |

*Miscellaneous*

| | | | |
|---|---|---|---|
| SK1 | Phono socket | SK2 | 2 way DIN type |

Printed circuit board
Heatsink
Wire, etc.

## Components for MOSFET Amplifier Power Supply (Figure 37)

### Capacitors
| | | | |
|---|---|---|---|
| C10 | 4700µF 40V tag ended electrolytic | C11 | 4700µF 40V tag ended electrolytic |

### Semiconductors
| | | | |
|---|---|---|---|
| D3 | 1N5402 | D4 | 1N5402 |
| D5 | 1N5402 | D6 | 1N5402 |

### Miscellaneous
| | |
|---|---|
| T1 | Standard mains primary, 26 – 0 – 26 volt 3.5 amp secondary or similar |
| LP1 | Panel neon indicator with integral series resistor for 240V main use |
| FS1 | 3 amp 20mm quick blow and chassis mounting holder |
| S1 | Rotary mains on/off switch |

Control knob

Mounting clips for C10 and C11

Wire, etc.

## 100W MOSFET Amplifier

Depending on the power supply used, this amplifier will give an output power of between about 50 and 100 watts RMS into an 8 ohm impedance load. Like the previous circuit it uses MOSFET power transistors in the output stage to give a high level of performance despite the relative simplicity of the circuit. The total harmonic distortion of the circuit is less than 0.05% provided the circuit is not overdriven, and the signal to noise ratio is better than 100dB.

### The Circuit

This circuit is based on a Hitachi design, and Figure 41 shows the full circuit diagram of the unit. Unlike the previous circuit, this one uses DC coupling to the loudspeaker and has dual balanced supplies with a central 0V and earth rail. This eliminates the need for a large output coupling capacitor plus the reduction in low frequency performance that this capacitor produces, and it also helps to give the circuit good supply ripple rejection.

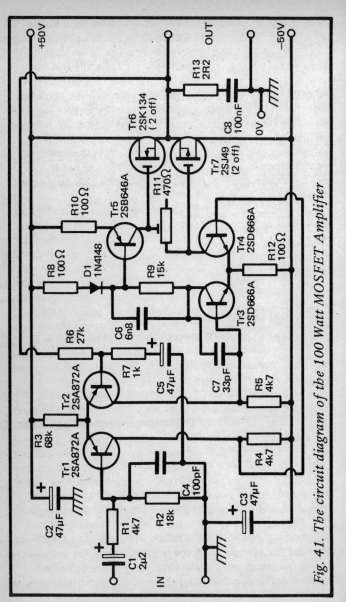

Fig. 41. The circuit diagram of the 100 Watt MOSFET Amplifier

Apart from the DC coupling, the configuration used in this circuit is quite different to that employed in the previous design.

The input and driver stages of the unit both use differential amplifiers. The input stage uses Tr1 and Tr2 while the driver stage is based on Tr3 and Tr4. Tr5 forms a constant current collector load for Tr4. The signal path through the amplifier starts with input coupling capacitor C1, and RF filter R1 — C4. R2 biases the input of the amplifier to the central 0V supply rail. Tr1 is effectively a common emitter amplifier with its output direct coupled to Tr4 which is used as a common emitter driver stage. From here the signal is coupled to Tr6 and Tr7 which are the complementary source follower output stage.

Negative feedback is taken from the output of the amplifer to the base of Tr2, and although there is no inversion of the signal from the base of Tr1 to the output of the unit, there is an inversion from the base of Tr2 to the output. This is due to Tr2 effectively acting as an emitter follower which drives the emitter of Tr1. With an input signal to the emitter of Tr1 this device effectively operates as a common base stage. Thus there is no inversion through Tr1 and Tr2, there is an inversion through Tr4, and there is no phase change through the output stage, so that the output of the amplifier and the base of Tr2 are out-of-phase and the required negative feedback is obtained. The values given to R6 and R7 give a voltage gain of about 28 times.

As was mentioned earlier, a slight drawback of power MOSFETs is that they are less efficient than bipolar transistors when used in a conventional Class B output stage, and their relative efficiency becomes somewhat worse in high power circuits where the high source currents require a gate to source voltage of several volts. The maximum output voltage swing is equal to the supply voltage less the maximum gate to source voltage of each transistor (if other more minor factors are ignored), and this obviously gives an output voltage swing which is far less than the supply voltage used.

A simple way of obtaining better efficiency is to simply use two identical devices connected in parallel for each output transistor. The maximum current handled by each output transistor is then approximately halved, and the maximum source to gate voltage of each device is reduced accordingly (with a corresponding increase in the output voltage swing of the amplifier).

This method can produce problems if tried with bipolar devices, and this is largely due to the positive temperature coefficient of these devices. If one output transistor tends to draw more current than the other (which is almost certain since the devices are not likely to be perfectly matched), one device becomes hotter than the other. This higher temperature results in the emitter − base threshold voltage of the transistor being reduced, and it consequently draws an even larger share of the output current. The device then becomes hotter, and this process continues until one output transistor is taking most of the output current while the other is largely ineffective.

This problem does not arise with power MOSFET transistors due to their negative temperature coefficient. If one device draws a higher output current than the other, the increase in its temperature causes an increase in the source to gate voltage needed for a given source current, and this device's share of the output current diminishes. In other words, rather than a tendency for the mismatch to be accentuated, the negative temperature coefficient has a stabilising effect. This makes it possible and completely safe to simply wire two power MOSFET in parallel without using any additional components to ensure accurate sharing of the output current.

*Power Supply*

A suitable power supply circuit for the 100 watt MOSFET amplifier is given in Figure 42.

This is very similar to the power supply circuit for the previous amplifier, but the centre tap on the supply at the junction of the two smoothing capacitors was formerly ignored. In this case this is used to give the central 0V earth supply, and the mains earth connects to this point in the circuit rather than to the negative supply rail. Fuses are included in both the positive and negative rails, of course.

The power obtained from the amplifier depends on the mains transformer used in the T1 position. For most purposes a 35 − 0 − 35 volt 160VA toroidal mains transformer should

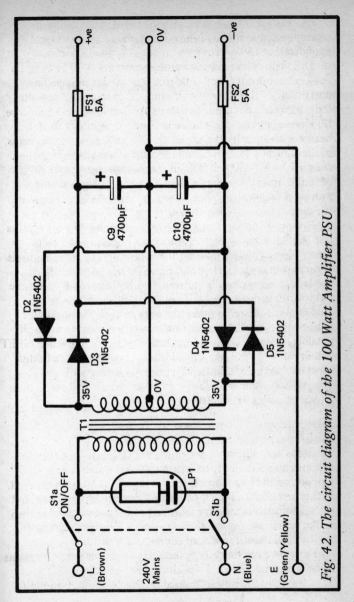

Fig. 42. The circuit diagram of the 100 Watt Amplifier PSU

91

suffice. For stereo operation either a transformer of the same voltage rating but a 300VA type should be used, or a separate supply using a 160VA component could be used for each channel. This gives a supply voltage of around ± 50 volts under quiescent conditions, but at full load the supply voltage falls substantially. This permits an output of up to about 70 watts RMS to be obtained using 8 ohm impedance loudspeakers.

Increased output power can be obtained by either using a mains transformer having a higher power rating, or one having a slightly higher secondary voltage, or a combination of the two. Using a 40 − 0 − 40 volt 300VA transformer (or a 500VA type for stereo operation) gives a supply potential of approximately ± 60 volts under quiescent conditions, and although the supply potential reduces somewhat at full load, the amplifier is nevertheless capable of comfortably providing 100 watts RMS into an 8 ohm impedance load. The use of a transformer having a voltage rating of more than 40 − 0 − 40 volts is not recommended.

An important point to note is that the 1N5402 rectifiers used in this circuit have a maximum current rating of 3 amps. This is sufficient for a single amplifier, but is inadequate for a stereo type. For stereo operation either a separate supply for each channel should be used, or the rectifiers must be replaced with higher power types. Individual rectifiers of suitable current rating do not seem to be readily available, but a bridge rectifier could be used instead. Any type having a voltage rating of 200 volts or more and a current rating of about 6 amps or more should be suitable.

## Construction

A suitable printed circuit design for the 100 watt MOSFET amplifier is shown in Figures 43 and 44. The four output transistors must be mounted on a large heatsink, and in the prototype a "Redpoint" type 4Y (4.5 degree Centigrade per watt) heatsink was used for each pair of output devices. Do not use heatsinks rated at less than 4.5 degree Centigrade per watt, and if a single heatsink is used for all four transistors it must obviously be a very large type rated at about 2 degrees Centigrade per watt or less.

The leads to the output transistors should be quite short, and

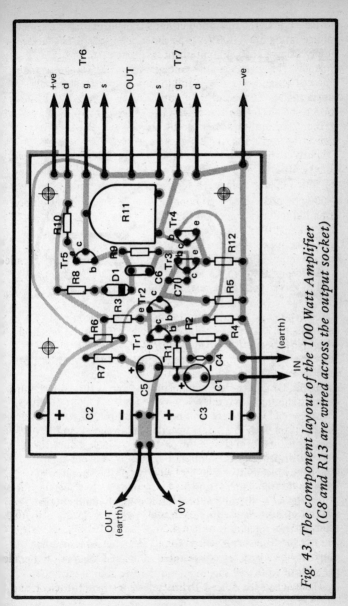

Fig. 43. The component layout of the 100 Watt Amplifier (C8 and R13 are wired across the output socket)

93

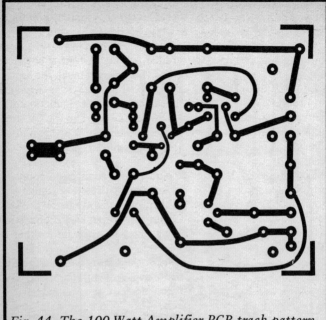

*Fig. 44. The 100 Watt Amplifier PCB track pattern*

preferably no more than about 50mm long. If they do need to be a little longer than this a low value resistor (about 68 ohms) can be added in the gate circuit of each output transistor. In conjunction with the input capacitance of each output device these resistors form simple lowpass filters which reduce the RF performance of the amplifier and helps to avoid high frequency instability. The performance of the amplifier at high audio frequencies would only be marginally affected by the addition of these resistors, and it is highly unlikely that they would introduce any discernable reduction in the reproduction quality.

The two transistors which form Tr6 are wired in parallel, with the two drain terminals being connected together, the two gate terminals wired together, and the two source terminals connected to each other. The two devices which form Tr7 are connected together in the same way. Note that C8 and R13 are wired across the output socket and are not included on the PCB design.

Probably the best method of construction to use for the power supply is straight forward hard-wiring, as for the power supply for the previous amplifier. The wiring is much the same as for this previous circuit (see Figure 40 for the wiring diagram), but the chassis and mains earth lead connect to the junction of the two smoothing capacitors (C9– and C10+), and the 0V supply output is taken from here. The only other change is that a fuse is included in the negative output of the unit as well as in the positive output.

The printed circuit design includes earth connection points for the input and output of the unit, and satisfactory results should be obtained using these. However, slightly better results may be obtained if the input and output earth connections are taken from the power supply at the take-off point for the 0V supply for the amplifier.

Incidentally, the type numbers of the transistors used in this and the previous amplifier design may seem a little unusual, but they are in fact Japanese type numbers and the specified devices are available from a few suppliers. The 2SB716 and 2SD756 are suitable alternatives for the 2SB646 and 2SD666 devices.

*Adjustment*

Before switching on the completed amplifier thoroughly check all the wiring a couple of times. In particular check the power supply wiring and the connections to the output transistors. Mistakes here could easily result in damage to the unit, and some of the more expensive components in the unit are amongst those which are most at risk. Start with R11 set in an almost fully counter-clockwise direction, and do not initially connect a loudspeaker to the output of the unit. Instead, connect a multimeter set to read a few volts (DC) FSD across the output to check that a low quiescent output voltage is present. Only a small fraction of a volt should be detectable, or possibly no DC voltage at all will be found. If a significant DC voltage is detected switch off the amplifier at once and recheck the wiring.

If all is well, connect a loudspeaker to the unit and give it an initial check. As for the previous design, R11 is adjusted for an increase in quiescent current consumption of about 100 milliamps. The current meter can be used to monitor either the positive or the negative supply when adjusting R11.

The amplifier requires an input of about one volt RMS in order to produce full output, and the input impedance is about 18 kilohms. The use of loudspeakers having an impedance of less than 8 ohms is not recommended.

## Components for 100 Watt MOSFET Amplifier (Figure 41)

*Resistors,* ¼ watt 5% except where noted

| | | | |
|---|---|---|---|
| R1 | 4k7 | R2 | 18k |
| R3 | 68k | R4 | 4k7 |
| R5 | 4k7 | R6 | 27k |
| R7 | 1k | R8 | 100 ohms |
| R9 | 15k ½ watt | R10 | 100 ohms |
| R11 | 470 ohms 0.25 watt horizontal preset | R12 | 100 ohms |
| R13 | 2R2 | | |

*Capacitors*

| | | | |
|---|---|---|---|
| C1 | 2µ2 63V radial electrolytic | C2 | 47µF 63V axial electrolytic |
| C3 | 47µF 63V axial electrolytic | C4 | 100pF ceramic plate |
| | | C6 | 6n8 mylar |
| C5 | 47µF 10V radial electrolytic | C8 | 100nF polyester |
| C7 | 33pF ceramic plate | | |

*Semiconductors*

| | | | |
|---|---|---|---|
| Tr1 | 2SA872A | Tr2 | 2SA872A |
| Tr3 | 2SD666A | Tr4 | 2SD666A |
| Tr5 | 2SB646A | Tr6 | 2SK134 (2 off) |
| Tr7 | 2SJ49 (2 off) | | |
| D1 | 1N4148 | | |

*Miscellaneous*
Printed circuit board
Heatsinks

Input and output sockets
Wire, etc.


*Components for 100W Amp. Power Supply Unit (Figure 42)*

*Capacitors*

| | | | |
|---|---|---|---|
| C9 | 4700µF 63V tag ended electrolytic | C10 | 4700µF 63V tag ended electrolytic |

*Semiconductors*

D2      1N5402
D3      1N5402          (See Text)
D4      1N5402
D5      1N5402

*Switch*

S1       Rotary mains switch

*Transformer*

T1       35 − 0 − 35 volt 300VA toroidal mains transformer
         (see text)

*Miscellaneous*

FS1     20mm quick-blow 5 amp fuse
FS2     20mm quick-blow 5 amp fuse
LP1 Panel mains indicator with integral series resistor for
mains use.
Chassis mounting fuseholders for FS1 and FS2, control knob,
mains lead, wire, etc.

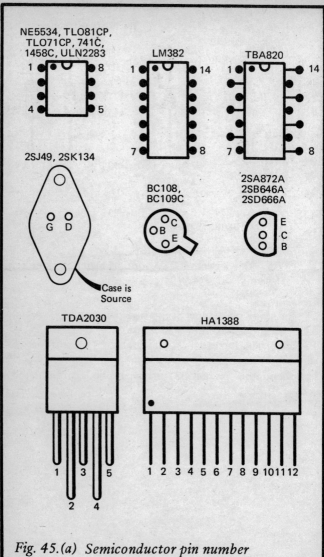

*Fig. 45.(a) Semiconductor pin number*
*(IC top views, transistor base views)*

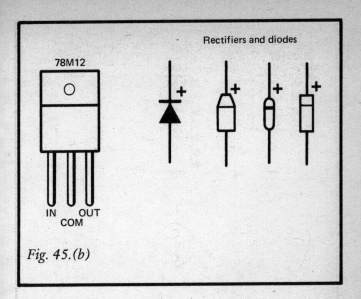

78M12

IN OUT
COM

Rectifiers and diodes

*Fig. 45.(b)*

*Notes*

Please note overleaf is a list of other titles that are available in our range of Radio, Electronics and Computer Books.

These should be available from all good Booksellers, Radio Component Dealers and Mail Order Companies.

However, should you experience difficulty in obtaining any title in your area, then please write directly to the publisher enclosing payment to cover the cost of the book plus adequate postage.

If you would like a complete catalogue of our entire range of Radio, Electronics and Computer Books then please send a Stamped Addressed Envelope to:

BERNARD BABANI (publishing) LTD
THE GRAMPIANS
SHEPHERDS BUSH ROAD
LONDON W6 7NF
ENGLAND